BRAINSTIM LLC

Rewired

"This book is dedicated to my mom who has persevered through unsurmountable odds and who possesses great strength and endurance. She reminds me daily to stay strong, endure, and that the essence of both your truth and your beauty comes from within. She is the reason for this workbook!"

Table of Contents

This workbook is not intended to replace proper medical care or professional supervision. There is no substitution for the expertise that can be provided by your physician, this book is intended to complement services in taking a holistic approach to the treatment of individuals with acquired brain injuries. This handbook is written to pick up where hospitals and treatment teams stop.

If you have any questions or concerns about any of the information in this handbook, please consult your health care provider.

The Stroke Recovery workbook, (level 1, Right Brain) is an introductory-level manual that focuses on cognitive deficits which are typically seen in injuries that affect the right side of the brain and the left side of the body. This curriculum has been developed with patients and caregivers in mind and to help restore functioning to these impaired areas of the brain.

BRAINSTIM LLC

Rewired

What is Cognitive Rehabilitation ?

Cognitive Rehabilitation is the process of restoring cognitive functions lost or altered as a result of damage to brain cells/chemistry. If areas of the brain can not be restored, new compensatory strategies can be taught. Cognitive rehabilitation can be taught through new methods ranging from education and process training to strategical and functional activities.

Cognitive Rehabilitation is an essential component of the rehabilitation process post acquired brain injury, yet is it underutilized. During the rehabilitation phase of treatment, therapists focus primarily on concrete areas to improve muscle function, tasks for activities of daily living, speech deficits, swallowing issues, and other forms of communication; Yet very little time to spend focusing on areas of cognitive restoration. These cognitive areas can include memory, comprehension, thinking, judgment (executive functions), and processing information. And while therapists perform assessments to determine the levels of cognitive function, they are not specifically trained nor are they required to intensively treat cognitive deficits.

Cognitive rehabilitation is a vital component in treatment after a brain injury. During injury, some areas in the brain can be damaged which can result in physical, cognitive, and emotional symptoms that we see post-injury. In health care settings the major push is physical therapy. Health care facilities can reimburse by insurances based on functional gains and so while cognitive rehabilitation therapy is needed and is invaluable, insurances currently do not bill for this needed service.

About the Author

Sarah Pearson -Collins is a Certified Rehabilitation therapist with a specialization in Brain Injury and Cognitive Rehabilitation. She is the founder and chief operating officer of the company BrainStim LLC, a company that specializes in providing cognitive rehabilitation services to individuals affected by acquired brain injuries. Sarah has worked in the clinical and research field for over 20 years, providing counseling, education, and support services to individuals and families affected by brain injury.

In May 2018, Sarah's passion for working with Individuals with head trauma intensified when both parents were involved in a devastating RV accident, leaving her mother with a brain hemorrhage and moderate stroke.

BRAINSTIM LLC

Rewired

Understanding Brain Injury

 Brain injury can be divided into two types; traumatic and non traumatic. A traumatic injury refers to on that is not degenerative or congenital , but primarily due some type of physical impact. Acquired or non traumatic is an injury that occurs after birth and not heredity , which result with changes in the brain.
 No two brain injuries are the same, therefore prognosis can vary by individual. There are three levels of severity when it comes to brain injury, mild, moderate and severe. Theses levels can range from a brief loss of consciousness to a prolonged unconscious state .
The brain is divided into 2 hemispheres, the right and left. The right hemisphere of the brain controls the left side of the body and the left hemisphere controls the right. Each hemisphere has 4 lobes, the frontal, temporal, occipital, and parietal. Each lobe has a unique cognitive function in the brain, but they all work together (see page 10). During a brain injury one or several areas can be affected causing an impairment in that particular area of the brain resulting in the loss of a function throughout the body.

There is still a lot to be learned about the brain , for example it was once thought that the brain could not heal after an acquired injury, and once those areas die, the brain could not function properly. Today's research shows that the brain has the ability to remodel, to create new cells, to learn and to use new pathways in order to restore functioning.

BRAINSTIM LLC
Rewired

| Acquired Brain Injury |

| Traumatic |

| Non Traumatic |

- ✓ Motor Vehicles accidents
- ✓ Falls
- ✓ Violence
- ✓ Military bomb blast
- ✓ Shaken baby syndrome
- ✓ Concussion

- ✓ Stroke
- ✓ Lack of oxygen Anoxia/Hypoxia
- ✓ Tumors
- ✓ Illness
- ✓ Infection

BRAINSTIM LLC

Rewired

Mild Brain Injury

- Brief loss of consciousness from a few seconds to a <30 minutes
- Post traumatic amnesia 1-24 hours
- Glasgow 13-15
- Normal brain imaging

Moderate Brain Injury

- Loss of consciousness from 1-24 hours
- Probable signs of trauma on brain scans
- Glasgow 9-12
- Possible bleeding, bruising fractures

Severe Brain Injury

- Loss of consciousness more than 24 hours
- Visible signs of trauma on brain scans
- Bruising or bleeding on brain
- Glasgow scale of 3-8

Glasgow Coma Scale
use to determine the severity of injury

Eye Opening Response

- Spontaneous--open with blinking at baseline 4 points
- To verbal stimuli, command, speech 3 points
- To pain only (not applied to face) 2 points
- No response 1 point

Verbal Response

- Oriented 5 points
- Confused conversation, but able to answer questions 4 points
- Inappropriate words 3 points
- Incomprehensible speech 2 points
- No response 1 point

Motor Response

Obeys commands for movement 6 points

Purposeful movement to painful stimulus 5 points

Withdraws in response to pain 4 points

Flexion in response to pain (decorticate posturing) 3 points •

Extension response in response to pain (decerebrate posturing) 2 points

• No response 1 point

EOR+VR=MR=Glasgow

Parts of the Human Brain

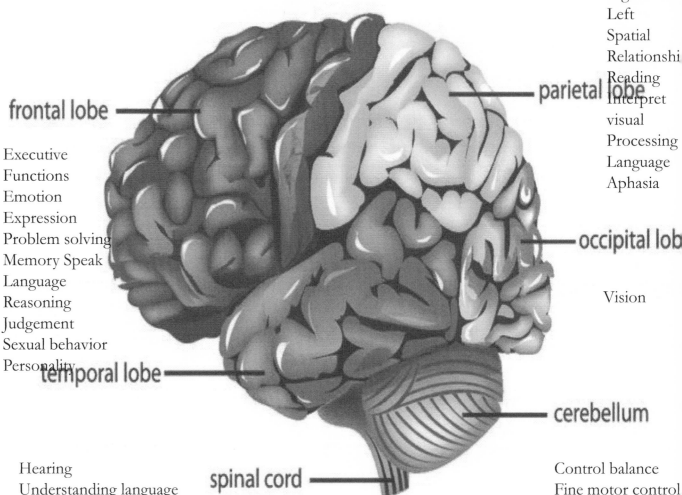

frontal lobe

Executive
Functions
Emotion
Expression
Problem solving
Memory Speak
Language
Reasoning
Judgement
Sexual behavior
Personality

temporal lobe

parietal lobe

Sensation
Procession
Right from
Left
Spatial
Relationshi
Reading
Interpret
visual
Processing
Language
Aphasia

occipital lob

Vision

cerebellum

spinal cord

Hearing
Understanding language
Role in emotions
Auditory stimuli

Controls messaging
between brain and
rest of body
Regulates breathing
Swallowing
Heart rate
BP
Consciousness

Control balance
Fine motor control
and Coordination
Motor learning
Regulates motor
Control posture

BRAINSTIM LLC

Rewire

Left Brain	Right Brain

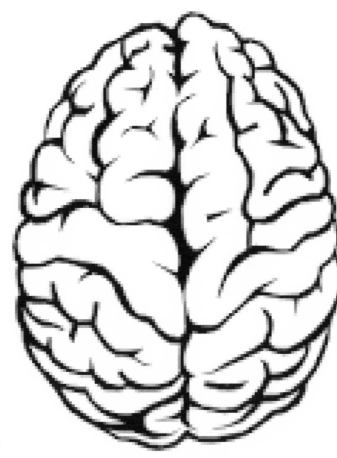

Left Brain

Analytic thought
Logic
Language
Detail oriented
Perception
Sequencing
Reasoning
Planning
Science
Written
Numerical skills
Caution
Verbal Skills
Rational thought
Math
Linear thinking
Facts
Right side motor
Right side vision

Right Brain

Art awareness
Creativity
Intuition
Insight
Holistic thoughts
Music awareness
Random sequencing
Emotional thought
Non verbal
Adventurous
Impulse
Imagination
Left side motor
Left side vison

BRAINSTIM LLC

Rewired

Left Brain

Left brain damage occurs on the left side of the brain but affects the right side of the body. The level of damage is dependent on several factors including the location of the obstruction, and how much tissue is affected. Because the damage can affect some areas of the brain, the severity can range from mild to severe cognitive deficits. Also, no two persons will experience brain injuries in the same manner and thus recovery varies.

Several deficits may result from a left-sided brain injury. Some of the impairments might be difficulty understanding language, (receptive skills), difficulty speaking(expressive language), heightened mood and reaction (anxiety depression), right-sided weakness, logic deficits, and sequencing, slow cautious behavior, and memory loss.

Right Brain

Damage that occurs on the right side of the brain but affects the left side of the body. The level of damage again is contingent on several factors as stated above with the left brain injury., However, some of the areas affected by the right brain injury might include left-sided weakness and or paralysis, impairments in visual-spatial perception, decreased awareness of self, altered creativity and music perception, visual memory deficits and quick inquisitive behavioral styles.

BRAINSTIM LLC

Rewired

As mentioned earlier, there are two hemispheres or sides of the brain. Each side controls many functions as stated earlier in this workbook. Depending on the side of the brain that has been injured, it can determine the areas of the brain that are impaired. Right hemisphere brain damage is damage to the right side of the brain (affecting the left side of the body), so your left side is generally affected and weakened due to the damage. Language is a major factor in most left-brain injuries, however, the right side controls attention, memory, reasoning, and problem-solving. Injuries to the right side of the brain may present as problems with how an individual thinks which may in turn lead to issues with communication deficits. Perception is also another deficit in individuals with right-sided brain injury in which he/she may not be aware of his or her problem. An Individual may also have attention issues, the inability to focus on specific tasks, issues with comprehension, perception due to left-sided neglect, reasoning, and problem-solving deficits. Memory is another common impairment. An individual may not remember previously learned information and may have a difficult time retaining new information. They may forget to complete a task Individuals with right-brain injuries may have difficulty understanding nonverbal cues and figurative language. Organizational deficits may also be impaired, problems with configuring information. This can cause problems when telling stories or giving directions and planning. Finally poor insight and difficulty with orientation can be seen in individuals with right-brain injuries (ASHA).

Orientation

BRAINSTIM LLC
Rewired

1. Is your name_____

2. Are you (age) _____ years old?

3. Is your birthday _____

4. Do you have _____ children

5. Are your children's name_____

6. Are you (single/married/divorced/widowed)?

7. Your spouses name is_____

8. Do you live on _____

9. I live in the city of _____

10. I live in the state of _____

1. Are you a man?
2. Are you awake or asleep?
3. Are you married?
4. Are you thirsty?
5. Do you have arms?
6. Point to your legs!
7. Are in at home?
8. Are you hungry?
9. Are you in a hospital?
10. Are you in a bed?
11. Are you at work?
12. Where are your eyes, nose, mouth.
13. Do you have fingers?
14. Can you wiggle your fingers?
15. Point to your knee
16. Can you smile?
17. Can you frown?
18. Do you have ears?
19. Point to your ears?
20. Where are your lips?

BRAINSTIM LLC

Rewired

1. Do you have hair?
2. Are you wearing pajamas?
3. Are you cold?
4. Are your eyes green?
5. Are you hungry?
6. Did you eat lunch?
7. Are you wearing lipstick?
8. Do elephants have trunks?
9. Do fish have feet?
10. Do dogs have beaks?
11. Can monkey's climb trees?
12. Do cars have wheels?
13. Can you touch the sky?
14. Do giraffes have spots?
15. Do women wear beards
16. Are you wearing a skirt?
17. Do cats have whiskers?
18. Do you live in a tent?
19. Do you have children?
20. Can you get milk from a horse?

BRAINSTIM LLC

Rewired

1. Do you eat breakfast at night?
2. Does a Dog say meow?
3. Do you hear with your eyes?
4. Is milk always fresh?
5. Does the Fed X guy deliver packages?
6. Do cops chase bad guys?
7. Can a chicken fly?
8. Can horses live in a house?
9. Does a watch tell time?
10. Can you milk a horse?
11. Do people eat paper when they are hungry?
12. Can you run as fast a s a bird can fly?
13. Can you hold your breath underwater for 10 minutes without an oxygen tank?
14. Can you read a newspaper?
15. Do you wear a bathing suit in the winter?
16. Do you wear a raincoat on a sunny day?

BRAINSTIM LLC
Rewired

Mark a F for fantasy or a R for reality in the following statements

1. A tree has many branches

2. The branches said hello

3. A cow makes milk

4. The dog made a pizza

5. The man shook my hand

6. The bird wrote a letter

7. A cat can type

8. The dog wore a dress

9. The cow jumped over the moon

10. You can buy clothes online

11. Water when cold turns to ice

12. Humans can fly without technology

13. Coals can turn to diamonds

14. A stork can deliver a baby

Memory/ Attention

Counting
Fill in the missing number

1		3		5		7	8	9	
	12	13			16			19	
21	22		24			27		29	
	32	33		35		37			40
	42		44			47	48		
51		53			56		58		
	62			65		67			70
	72		74			77			

All kind of Shapes

Identify each shape by marking the name next to it

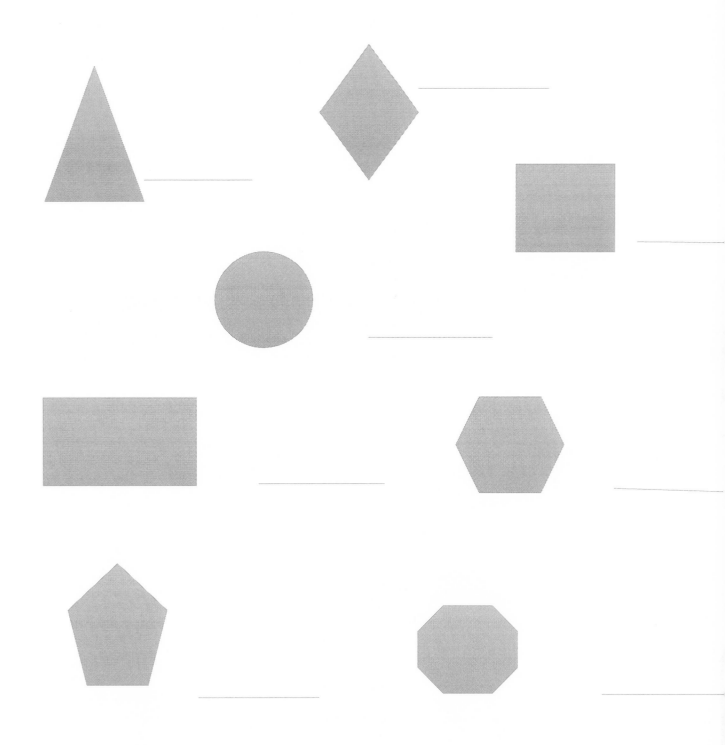

Circle Triangle Diamond Square Rectangle Hexagon Octagon
Pentagon

More Shapes

Identify each shape by coloring all triangles red and all squares yellow.

Music in the Air

Match the instruments on the left with the instruments on the right

Transportation

Match the items on the left column with the item on the right

Matching

Match the items on the left column with the item on the right

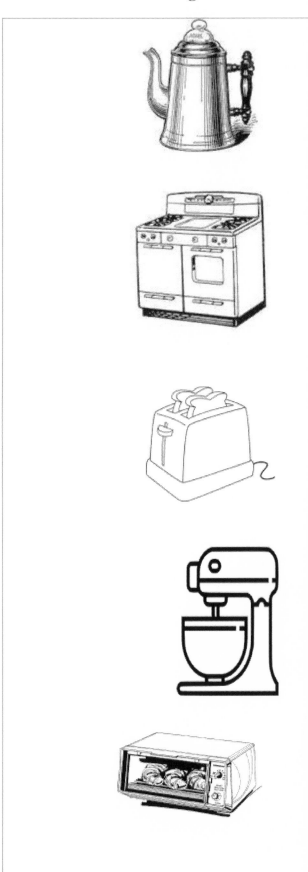

Matching

Match each object to the highlighted word

Microwave

Blender

Mop/bucket

Toaster Oven

Vacuum

Pot

Dustpan

Clothing

Match each object to the word highlighted in the middle.

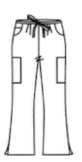

Pants
Bra
Women
underwear
Shirt

Skirt
Shoes
Shorts
Boxers

Pantyhose
Hat
Blouse
Socks

Kitchen Items

Read each word and match the word with the object below

Pan	Cup	Pot

Bowl	Spoon	Sink

Let's Have a Picnic

Read each word and match the word with the object below

Wine	Cheese	Pie	Corn

Hotdogs	Grapes	Sandwich

Matching

Match each animal with their home

Matching

Draw at line from the item on the left to the item on the right with at direct relationship

Origins

Draw at line from the item on the left to the item on the right with at direct relationship

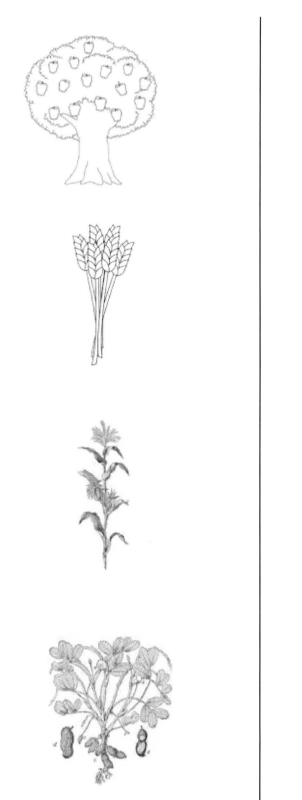

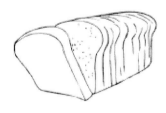

What are you eating?

Pair each animal with the foods that they eat

Can you Find the Differences?

Find the item that is different in each group

Can you Find the Differences?

Find the item that is different in each group

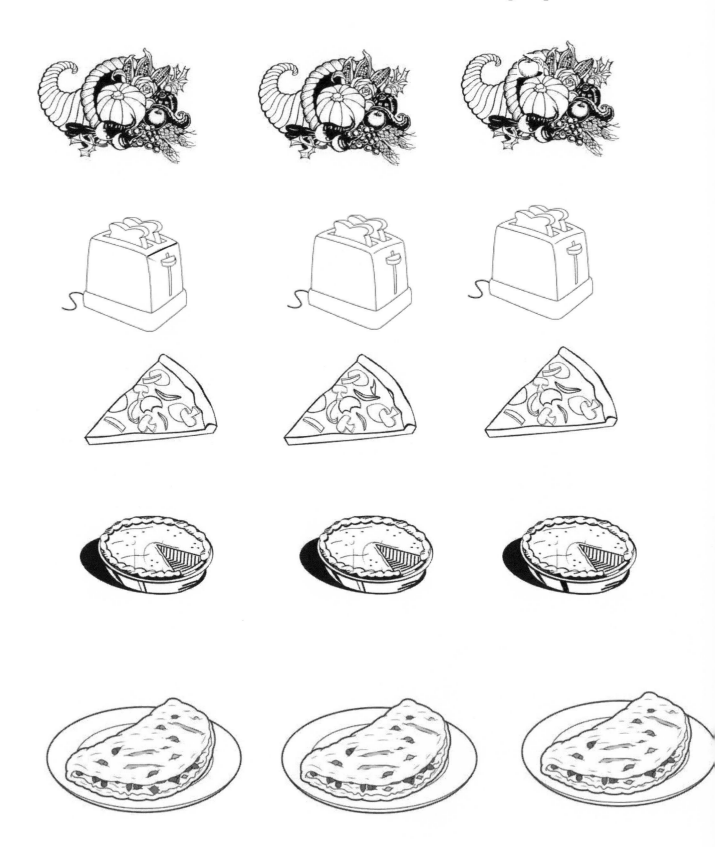

Day and Night

What Can you see during the Day?

_____

_____

What Can you see during the Night?

_____

_____

Moon   Clouds   Birds   Bats   Sun   Stars

It's Cold Outside

Which Of these items does not represent winter

Emotions

Pair the emotion from the word to the correct emotion in the picture

Excited   Angry   Happy   Sad   Bored

Scared

The Holidays

Identify each holiday using the words in the key below

Christmas	Easter	Thanksgiving	Valentines Day

New Year   Hanukah

Chinese New Year   Independence Day

Who Are We?

Match the pictures with the respective names below

Mother Theresa	Queen Victoria II	Abraham Lincoln
Martin Luther King	John f Kennedy	Nelson Mandela
Marilyn Monroe	Marilyn Monroe	Malcolm X
	Mahatma Gandhi	

Whose Hat it this?

Draw a line from the hat to the title of that person wears it

Belongs to a
- Pilot
- Chef
- Police officer
- Queen
- Construction Worker
- Captain
- Graduate
- Cowboy
- Aristocrat
- Baseball player
- Shriner
- Fisherman

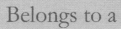

Planes Trains Automobiles

Answer the following using the pictures below

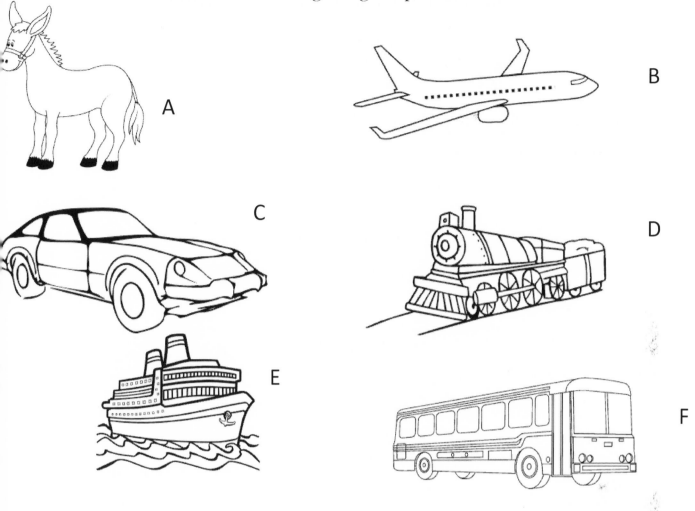

1. What Method(s) of transportation can be used to travel from Florida to the Bahamas?
2. What method of transportation can be used to travel in the desert?
3. What method of transportation can be used to travel very fast from one city to another?

Going on a Cruise

Circle the items that you would take on a Caribbean cruise

Hygiene

Discuss how each of these objects are used

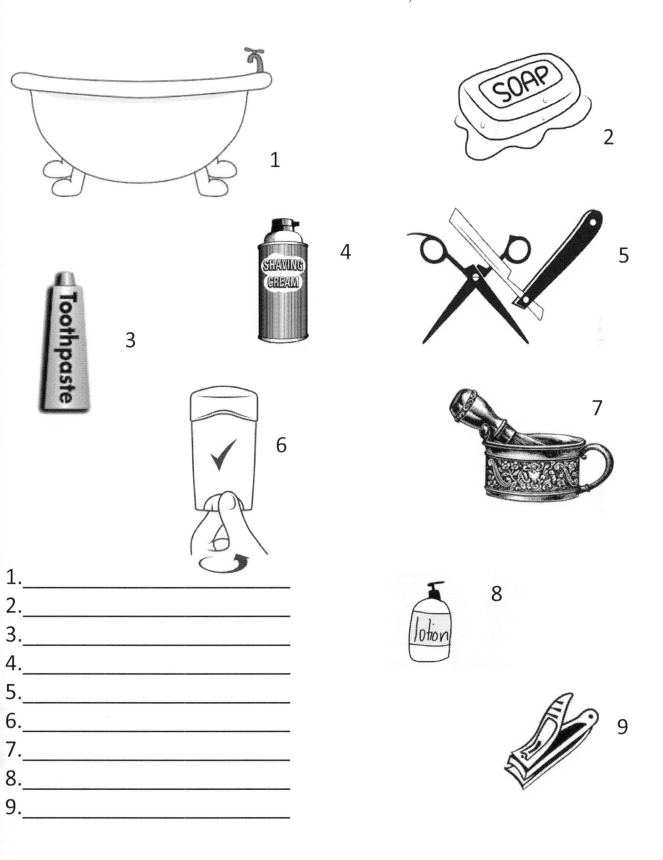

1. _____

2. _____

3. _____

4. _____

5. _____

6. _____

7. _____

8. _____

9. _____

Hygiene

Draw a line from the object on the left to the matching number of item(s) on the righ

It's Raining

Identify by circling the items that should be worn in the rain

Relationships

Pair the objects on the right with the objects in the left column

Spring Has Sprung
Circle the images that best represent spring

Sports

Using the Balls below, draw a line to the equipment that best represent each sport

 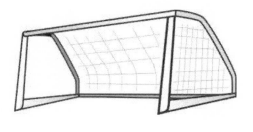

Sports

Using the Balls below, draw a line to the equipment that best represent each sport

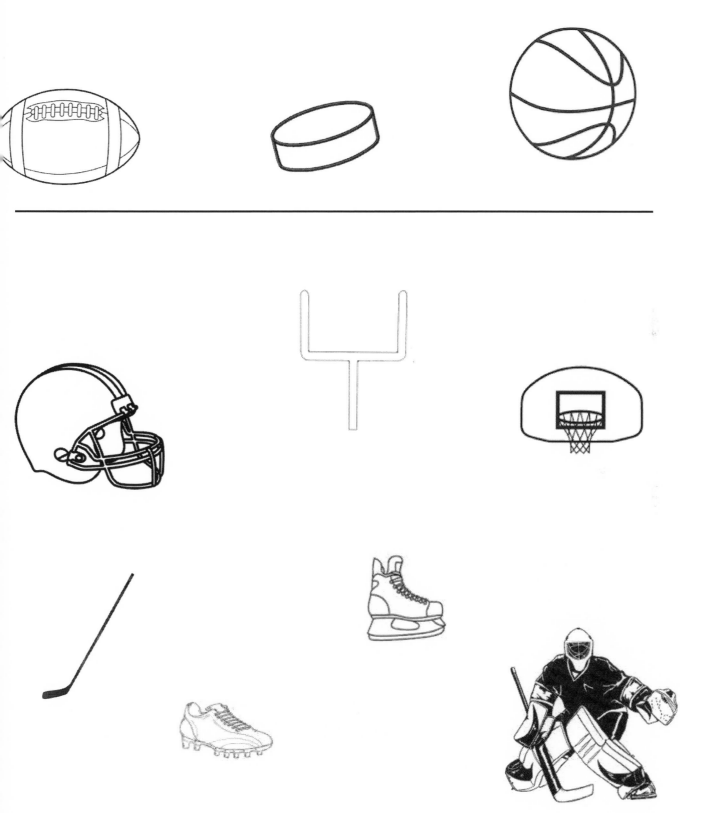

Counting Exercise

Draw a line from the box to the matching number of items

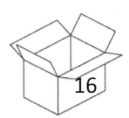

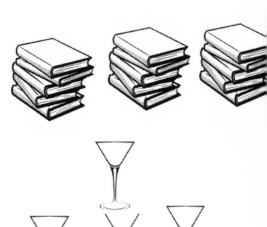

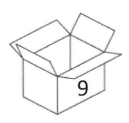

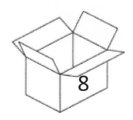

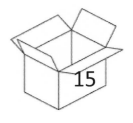

Counting Exercise

Draw a line from the box to the matching number of items

7

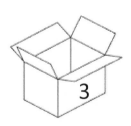

5

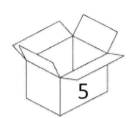

3

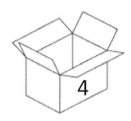

4

Measurement

Number each item from the shortest (1) to the longest (5)

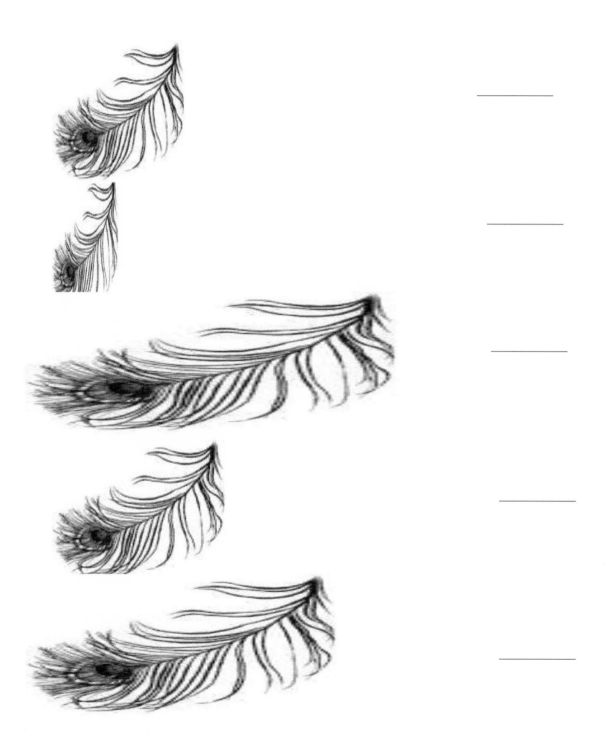

_____

_____

_____

_____

_____

The Ruler

Cut out the ruler at the bottom of the page . Use it to measure the length in centimeters of each object.

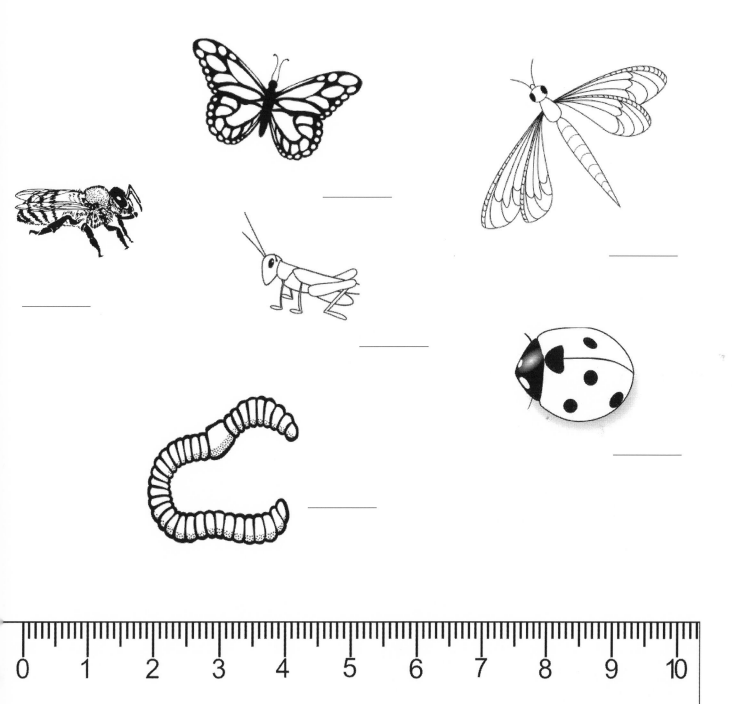

The Ruler

Cut out the ruler at the bottom of the page . Use it to measure the length in inches of each object.

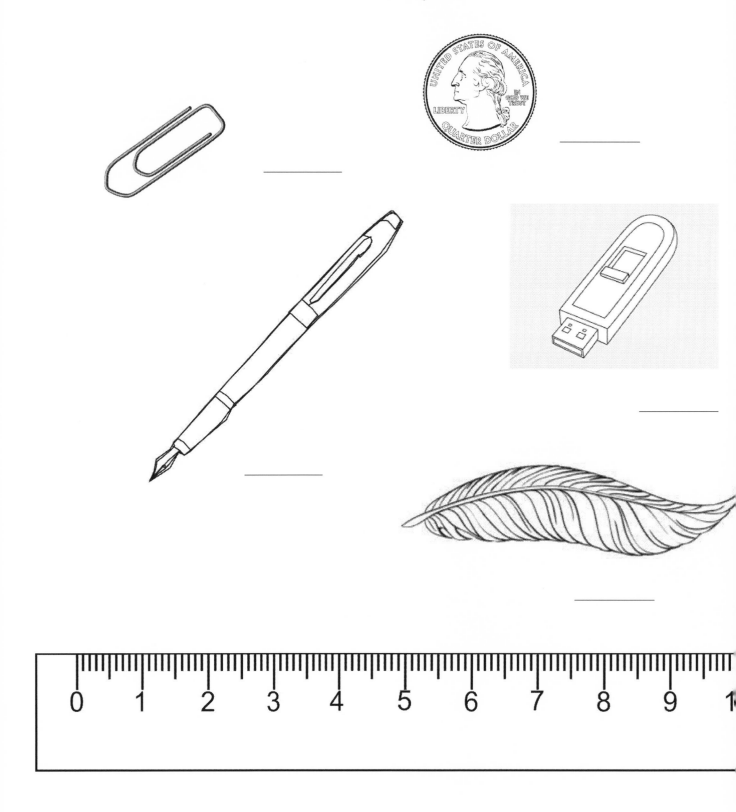

Broken Clock

Please help us fix the clock by filling in the missing numbers

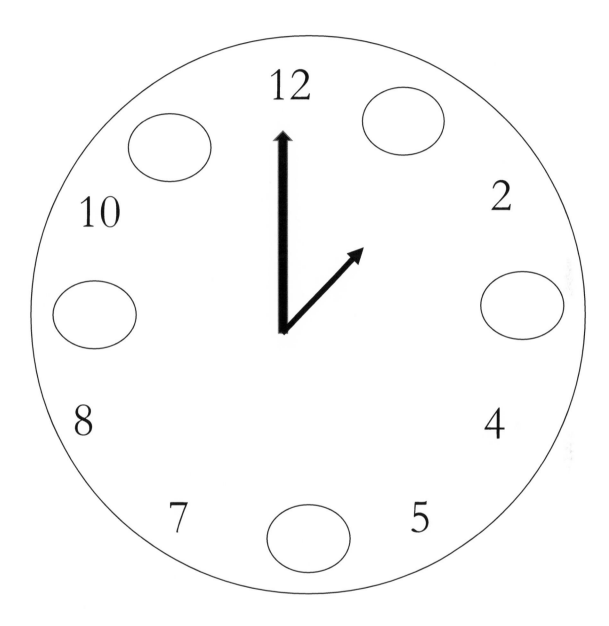

What Time is it?

Write the time below of each clock

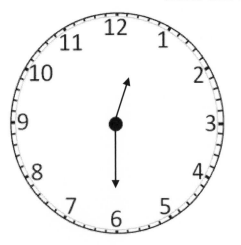

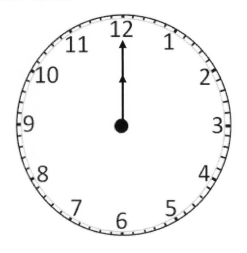

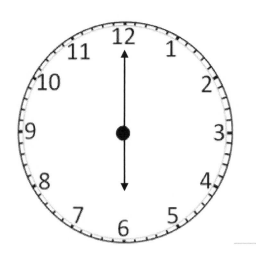

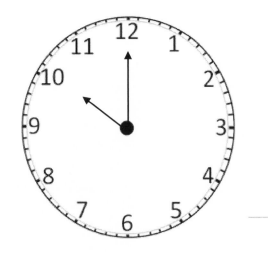

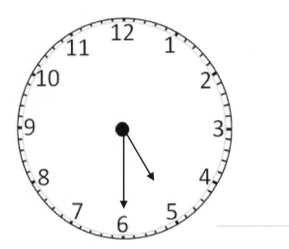

What Time is It?

Draw Hands according to the appropriate time

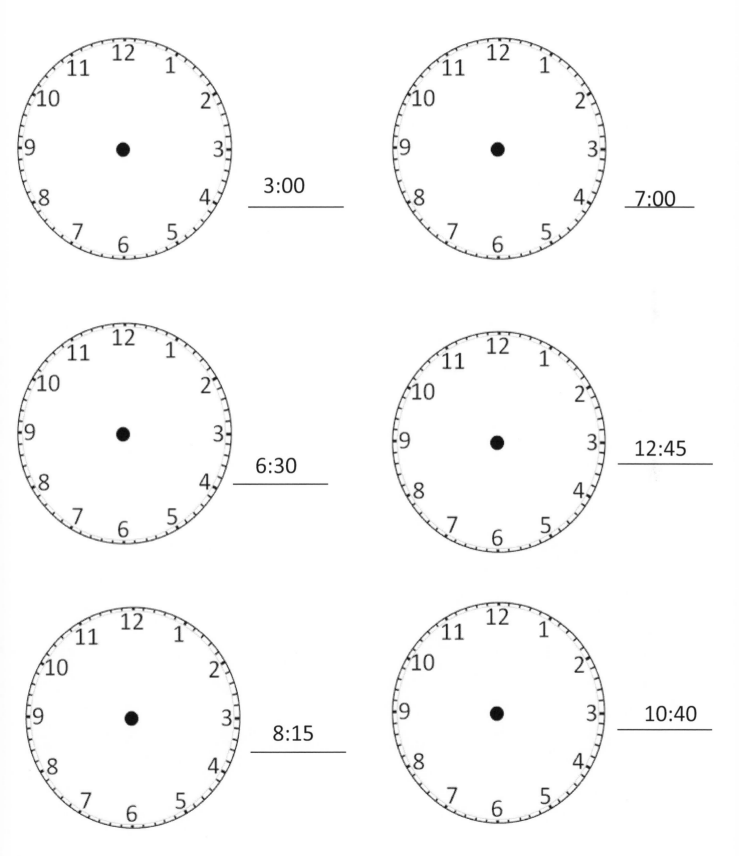

3:00

7:00

6:30

12:45

8:15

10:40

What time is it?

Write the time below of each clock

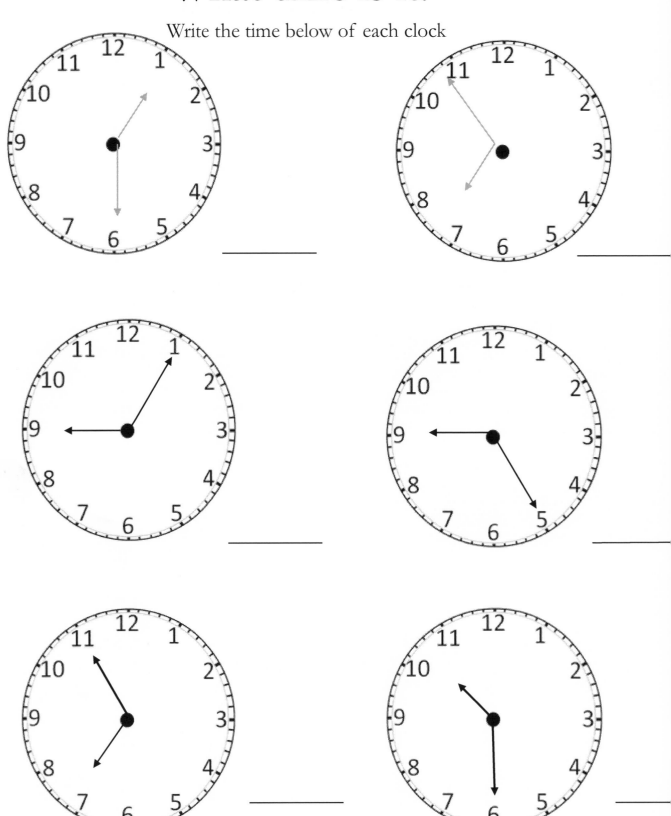

_____

_____

_____

_____

_____

_____

What time is it?

Write the time on the line below each clock

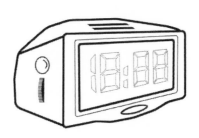
Seventeen minutes past ten O'clock

_____

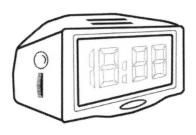
Thirty-three minutes past six O'clock

_____

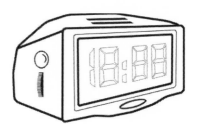
Noon

_____

Fifteen minutes to one O'clock

_____

Show Me the Money!

Write the money value on the line provided

_____   _____   _____

_____

Show me the Money
Write the money value.

_____

_____

_____

_____

Pick the Right Price

Read the price on each vase . Draw a line to the money you need to buy it.

$.85

$.77

$1.30

Pick the Right Price

Read the price on each vase . Draw a line to the money you need to buy it.

 $.75

 $.30

 $.50

Name Your Price

Give an approximate value to the items below using the values in the key.

 Lottery
Ticket

 Prince
Concert

 24 pack

 Steak Dinner
$$$

 Gallon of Milk

$31.99

$150.00

$1.00

$2.69

$55.00

Name Your Price

Give an approximate value to the items below using the values in the key.

Value Meal

_____

$100.00

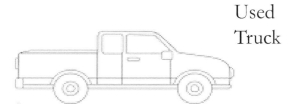

Full cart of groceries

_____

$6,500.00

$45.00

Used Truck

_____

$6.00

$15.00

Full Tank

_____

Hair Cut

_____

Name Your Price

Give an approximate value to the items below using the values in the key.

_____

_____

_____

_____

_____

_____

_____

_____

_____

$.50	$1.00	$2.00
$3.00	$4.00	$5.00

Behind

Circle the objects that are behind

On Top

Circle the objects that are on top

Under

Circle all of the items that under

Signs
Identify the appropriate signs using the phrases below

- Merge to the right
- Two way traffic
- Means to Halt
- Speed limit to not exceed 45mph
- No trucks allow
- Slippery driving
- Do not Enter
- Give the right away
- Crossroad ahead

Signs

Identify the appropriate signs using the phrases below

- Men's bathroom
- No smoking area
- Family restroom
- No cell phones Allowed
- Please Recycle
- Women's bathroom
- Steep, watch step
- This way out
- Slippery

Toilets

WOMEN

Signs
Identify the appropriate signs using the phrases below

Hotel　　School　　　Hospital　　　airport　　　Bus
　　Playground　　Gas Station　　Food　　　　Parking　No Parking
　　　　Women Rest Room　　　　Camping

Safety

Identify the appropriate signs using the phrases below

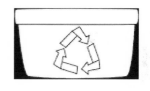

- Do not litter
- Poisonous
- You will be
- Train crossing
- One way
- No bicycles allowed
- Winding road
- Road shared by horse and buggy
- Do not proceed
- Hazardous materials
- Traffic goes in only one direction
- Be careful
- Fire extinguisher location

What's in Your Refrigerator

Circle the item(s) that belong in the refrigerator?

What's in the Wash

Circle all of the items that do not belong in the washing machine

Make a Egg Sequencing

Number 1-5 the order of operation beginning at what happened first

Planting Sequencing

Number 1-5 the order of operation beginning at what happened first

Folder Sorting

Read each word and place in the appropriate folder

Shirt	Grapes	Black	Green
Apple	Sock	Blouse	Banana
Orange	Blue	Purple	Nightgown
Pants	Avocado	Pineapple	White
Red	Watermelon	Mulberry	Stocking
Tie	Bra	Skirt	Camisole

Clothes

Fruit

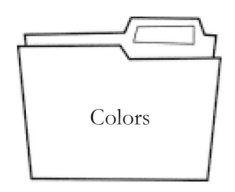

Colors

Recycle

Place items in the appropriate recycling bin

Folder Sorting

Read each word and place in the appropriate folder

Tire	August	Thursday	Bed
Monday	Friday	Chair	June
Sad	Happy	Rug	Wednesday
Depressed	Muffler	Brakes	Angry
Steering	July	Motor	Stressed
wheel	Wiper	September	Frustrated
February	Saturday	Sunday	Television

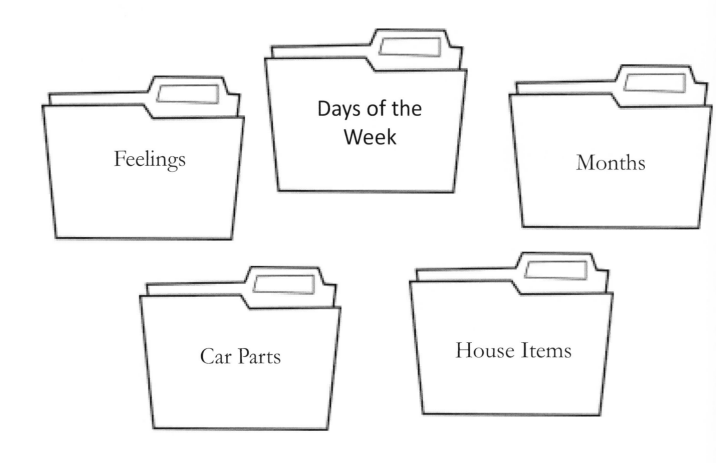

Feelings

Days of the Week

Months

Car Parts

House Items

What am I?

Sort each animal in the correct classification

Mammal

Bird

Reptile

What am I?

Sort each item in the correct classification

Comprehension

Sequence Writing

Using the pictures below identify each step of the task of washing clothes. Write each step below

Let's do the Laundry

1. First I am going to _____
2. Next, I am going to _____
3. Next I am going to _____
4. Next I am going to _____
5. Last, I am going to _____

- Sort clothes
- Add laundry detergent
- Place clothes in dryer 45-50 minutes
- Turn on washing machine
- Fold clothes

Sequence Writing

Identify each step of making a cake using the key below. Write each step on the lines provided

Let's bake a cake

Ingredients
1._____
2._____
3._____
4._____

1. _____
2. _____

Bake
1. _____
2. _____

Cooling
1. _____
2. _____

- Eggs
- Margarine/oil
- Water
- Empty content into a bowl

- Mix all ingredients for 2 minutes
- Pour mixed batter into a cake pan
- Place in oven of 35-40 minutes

- Icing cake
- Let cool for 10-15 minutes
- Flour
- Heat oven to 350°

Music Everywhere

Read each statement and use to identify the musical instrument

Joe is playing the violin

George is playing the drums

Layla is playing the flute

Jessica plays the piano

Calendar Orientation Exercise
Use calendar to answer the following questions

1. What is the month

2. How many Fridays are in this month

3. Circle the last day of the month

4. How many days are in this month

5. What date is the third Thursday

6. What is the date of the second Monday

7. Put an X on the fourth Wednesday

8. How many ways are in this month

9. What day does the first fall on

10. What day of the week is the 20

Measurements

Answer the questions about the liquid volume. Show your work

1 gallon=4 Quarts   1Quart= 2 pints   1Pint=2 Cups   1Cup=8 Ounces

Stephen drank 1 pint of coffee for lunch. How many cups of coffee did he drink?_____

Sarah started her morning water intake with a gallon of water; divided into four parts. How much does each container hold?_____

Ezra added a half cup of butter to the brownie mixture, how many ounces did he add _____

Mrs. Wells, brought 2 quarts of orange juice at the market, how many cups will she have to give to her children?_____

Inferences

Inferences is a Conclusion reached based on evidence and reasoning.

What inference can be drawn from the following statements?

Josiah is very happy after unwrapping his birthday gift.

There are muddy paw prints on the new carpet.

Inferences

Inferences is a Conclusion reached based on evidence and reasoning.

What inference can be drawn from the following statements?

1.

Sarah left a several shopping bags on the floor in the house and is walking around in her new dress

2.

Stephen see a milk puddle next to the refrigerator and see Josiah with a milk mustache

1. _____

2. _____

Inferences

Inferences is a Conclusion reached based on evidence and reasoning.

What inference can be drawn from the following statements?

1.

Mr. Johnston is extremely excited and jumping up and down shouting "hoo-ray" while holding his lottery ticket .

2.

James walked into the grocery with mud all over his boots.

1. _____

2. _____

Inferences

Inferences is a Conclusion reached based on evidence and reasoning.

What inference can be drawn from the following statements?

1.

Mr. Parker is seen leaving the hospital in a wheelchair with a cast on his leg

2.

Ms. Jones Looked inside the desk, under the bed and on top of the refrigerator for the keys.

1. _____

2. _____

Over the last 3 months, the member of St Christopher's church has been collecting items to be recycled. The graph below represents each recycled item that was turned in.

Saint Christopher's Recycling Fundraising Dive

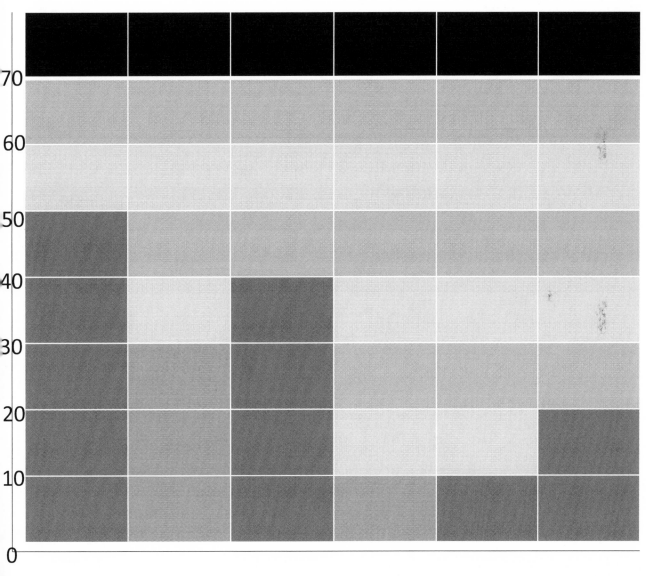

Using the graph on the previous page to answer questions below

1. How many aluminum and glass items were recycled
2. How many more plastic items were recycled then metal/other?
3. Which recycled item was brought in the most?
4. What was the total number of glass and plastic?
5. If this fundraiser went on for 3 more month, estimate how much cardboard would have been recycled?
6. If this fundraiser went on for 3 more month, estimate how much glass an aluminum would have been recycled?

Vaping Can Be Addictive Panel Concludes and May Lure Teenagers to Smoking, Science

Jan.23.2018

WASHINGTON — A national panel of public health experts concluded in a report released on Tuesday that vaping with e-cigarettes that contain nicotine can be addictive and that teenagers who use the devices may be at higher risk of smoking.

Whether teenage use of e-cigarettes leads to conventional smoking has been intensely debated in the United States and elsewhere. While the industry argues that vaping is <u>not a </u>steppingstone to conventional cigarettes or addiction, some antismoking advocates contend that young people become hooked on nicotine, and are enticed to use cancer-causing tobacco-based cigarettes over time.

1. Who is this article about?
2. What is this article about?
3. When did this article come out?
4. Where is this happening?
5. Why is this happening?
6. How are youth becoming hooked on nicotine?

Australia weather: Monsoon rains cause floods in Queensland

Feb 2, 2019

Exceptional monsoon rains have caused severe flooding in parts of Australia's north-eastern state of Queensland.

Cars and livestock have been swept away over a large area around the coastal city of Townsville. Emergency crews are evacuating people on rafts.

Up to 20,000 homes could be flooded if the downpours continue, officials warn.

A dam has reached twice its capacity and water is being released to avoid putting further strain on it. More rain is expected in the coming days.

Northern Queensland has a tropical climate and experiences monsoon rain from December to April. But the current conditions in the Townsville area are rare.

"We have not been in this situation before," Queensland Premier Annastacia Palaszczuk is quoted as saying by the Australian Broadcasting Corporation (ABC).

"There has been a lot of rain falling over the Townsville catchment and some of these levels are unprecedented."

Who is Queensland Premier?

What is happening in this article?

When did this event take place?

How many homes could be affected?

How is the city dealing with this crisis?

Why is the city flooding?

Opposites

Draw a line to the object representing the opposite

Opposites

Draw a line to the object representing the opposite

Antonym

Find the word that means the opposite of

Light	Depressed
alike	Dark
Happy	Exit
Bottom	Top
Entrance	Exterior
Interior	Smooth
Rough	speechless
Communicate	Different

Antonym

Find the word that means the opposite of

Cowardly	Unsteady
Vanish	Brave
Private	Appear
Faithful	Public
Forward	Shy
Loyal	Arrogant
Humble	Unreliable
Sleep	Awake

Draw a line to the words that describes the word in the middle

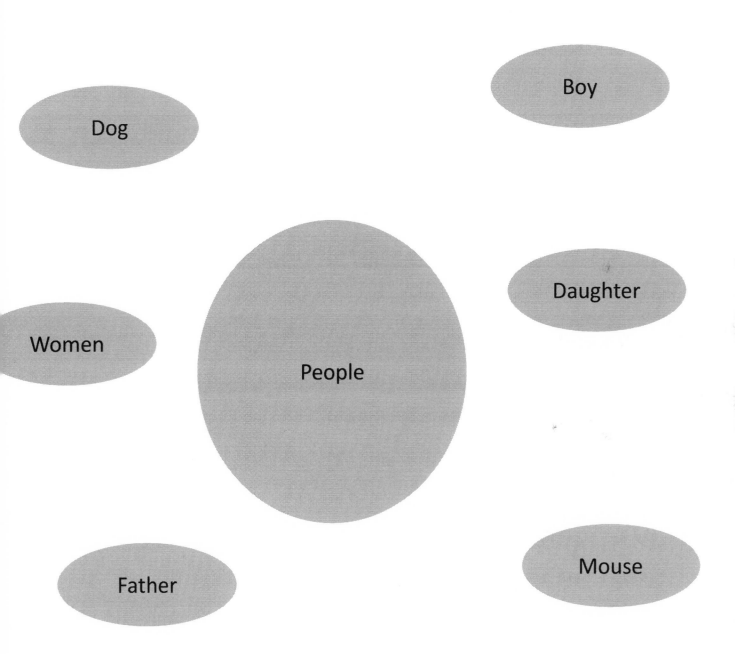

Dog

Boy

Women

Daughter

People

Father

Mouse

Draw a line to the words that describes the word in the middle

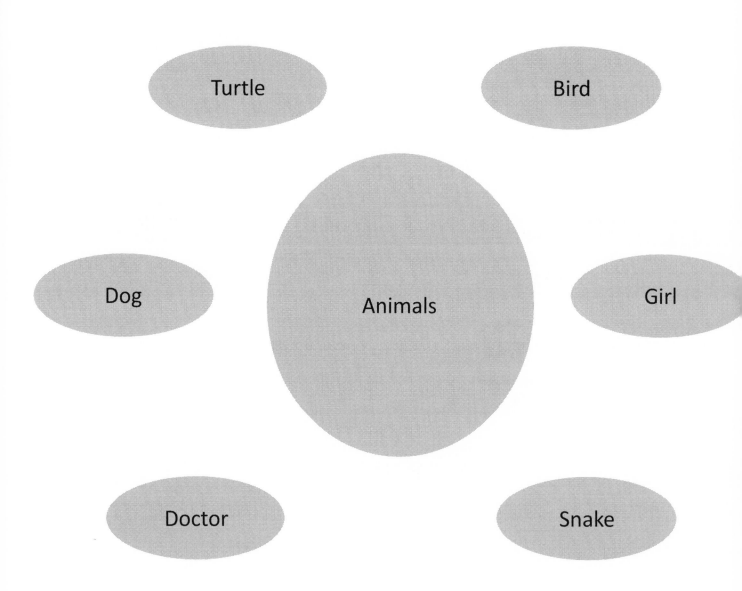

Turtle

Bird

Dog

Animals

Girl

Doctor

Snake

Synonyms
Draw a line to the words that describes the word in the middle

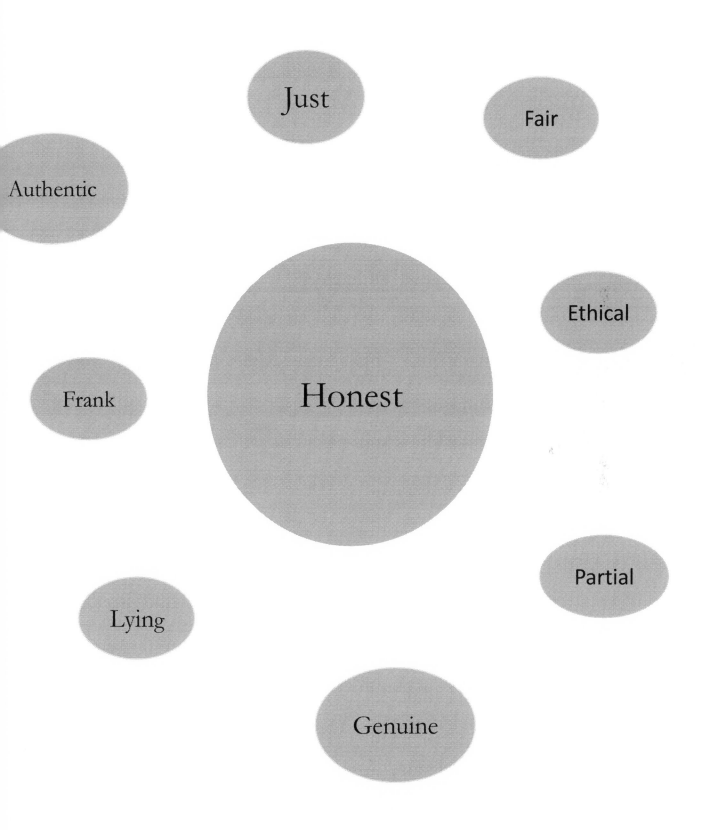

Synonyms

Draw a line to the words that describes the word in the middle

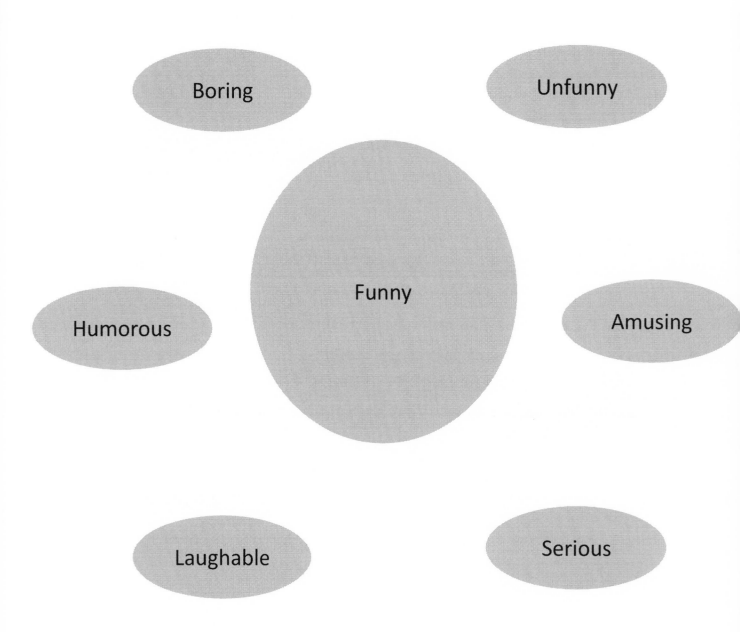

Boring

Unfunny

Humorous

Funny

Amusing

Laughable

Serious

Synonyms
Find the word that means the same

Fatal	Lockup
Common	Ground
Bottom	Familiar
Unkind	Deadly
Jail	Gaze
Light	Cruel
Stare	Morning
Skinny	Thin

Describe This?

Give a brief definition/description of the following terms

Duck _____

Goat _____

Dog _____

Cat _____

Bowl _____

Spoon _____

Hat _____

Cheese _____

Apple _____

Pie _____

Describe This!

Give a brief definition/description of the following terms

Above

Again

Mr. /Mrs.

Give

Funny

House

Yours

Wash

Think

Sorry

Describe This!

Give a brief definition/description of the following terms

Harvest

Refund

Ignore

Concentrate

Reject

debate

Renew

Generous

Celebrate

Competition

Describe This!

Give a brief definition/description of the following terms

Yesterday _____

Edge _____

Travel _____

Opinion _____

Compare _____

Emphasize _____

Carefully _____

Instrument _____

Region _____

Persuade _____

Describe This!

Give a brief definition/description of the following terms

Within

Large

Follow

Before

Under

Important

Soon

Later

Understand

Between

Fact and Opinion

Read each statement. Place a X if the statement is a fact or a opinion

	Fact	Opinion
A bicycle has two wheels		
Dog is a man's best friend		
Albany is the capital of New York		
Nobody likes pinto beans		
Debate is another word for talk		
A group of birds is called a flock		
Canada is north of the United States		
The Buffalo Bills are awesome		
Plants need water in order to grow		
Apples are the best fruit		
Barack Obama is the 44th president of the United States		
The earth is round		
Florida is the best state		

Fact versus Non-Fiction

Read each statement. Place a X on the respective line

HINT** non-fiction – (real events, real people)

	Fiction	Non-Fiction
1. Little Red Riding Hood		
2. The autobiography of George Washington		
3. An article about how to grow a garden		
4. A football trade card with stats on the back		
5. Introduction to Biology		
6. The Prince of Niccolò Machiavelli		
7. Alice and Wonderland		
8. Diary of Anne Frank		
9. Hamlet		
10. Cartoons in the newspaper		
11. A short story		
12. The assignation of John F Kennedy		

Compare and Contrast

Read the paragraph and then compare and contrast in the diagram below

Similarities   Differences

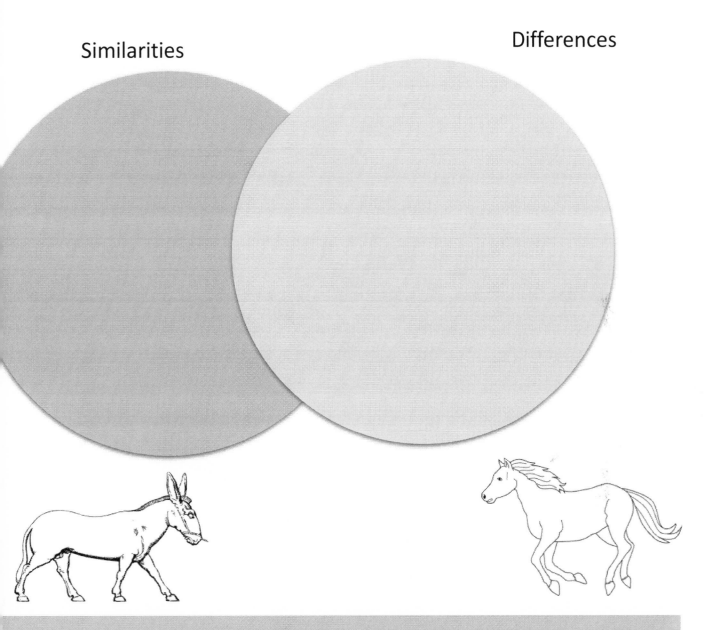

Horses and Donkey are not very similar. Although they both have four legs and evolve from the Equidae, they have a lot of differences. For instance horses are fast, easy to train and agile. They have a thin coats, short ears and long manes and tails . Donkeys on the other hand are intelligent but harder to train, able to carry 2x their weight, they have thicker coats, shorter tails, and long ears.

Compare and Contrast

Read the paragraph and then compare and contrast in the diagram below

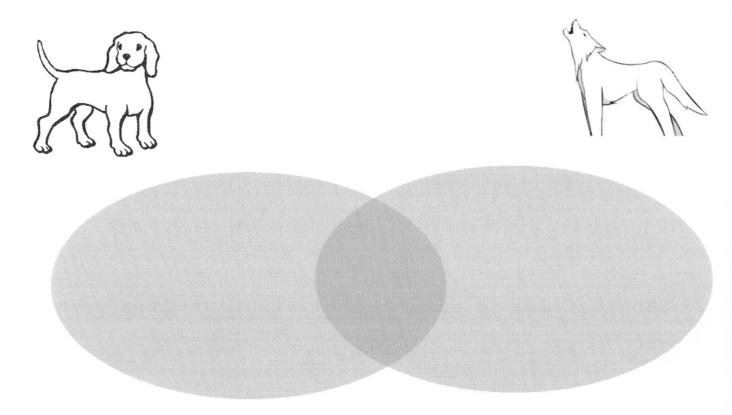

Wolves and Dogs have many things in common. They both have animals that live all over the world. Another similarity is that they both have four legs, and both have fur. Wolves like dogs do form packs but only wolves hunt in packs. Both wolf and dogs can live outdoors, but dogs are domesticated and can live in doors as well. Finally, wolves are primarily carnivores.

Answer the questions using the graph below

SURVEY ON FAVORITE VEGETABLES
Elderberry Skilled Nursing Home

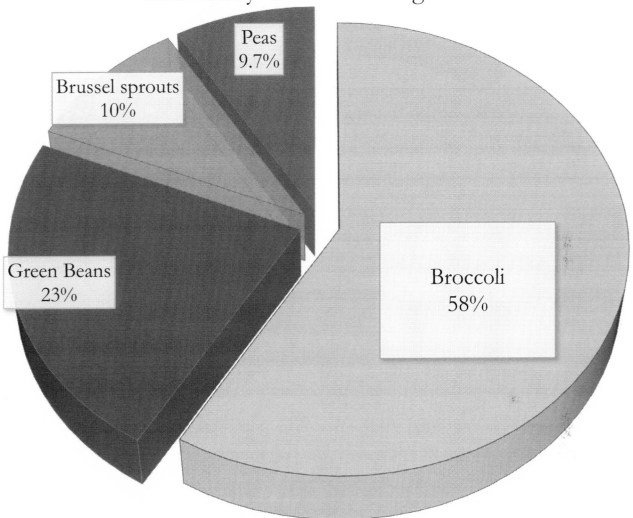

1.This pie chart gives data about what?

2. The second largest section of the graph represents what?

3. What percentage of the patients like green beans?

4. Almost 10% of the patients like what vegetable?

5. What percentage of the populations would like peas and brussels sprouts?

Using the graph below answer the questions

Buffalo Winter Driving

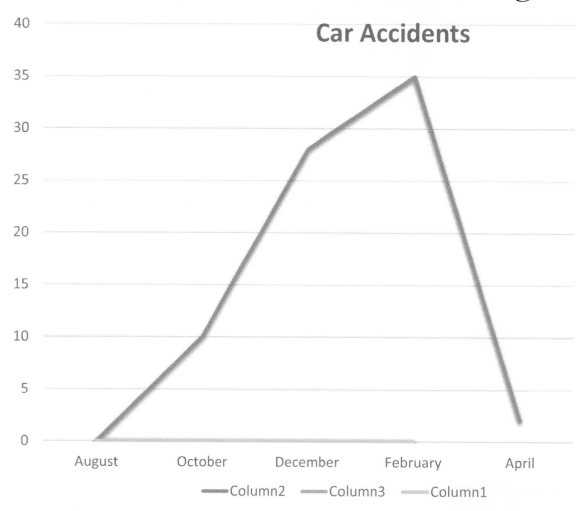

Car Accidents

1. The line graphs represents the relationship between what two things?
2. How many accidents did Buffalo have in the month of October?
3. As the weather got colder in December where there more or less accidents?
4. What happened in April as the weather got warmer?

Tables of Contents

Answer the questions using the table of contents

1. On which page can you find the recipe for pecan waffles?
2. What page should to turn to for more information about fritters
3. If you are looking for direction on how to make biscuits , which page should you read?
4. If you are interested in learning more about cooking which page should you read?
5. What does it talk about on page 25?

Hockey Playoff Schedule

Answer the questions using the hockey play off schedule

TEAMS	RINK	DATE	TIMES
Sabers vs. Eagles	Buffalo	Sunday	1:00
Giants vs Jays	Akron	Wednesday	7:30
Bulls vs Saints	Ontario	Saturday	7:00
Glaciers vs Reds	Buffalo	Friday	8:00
Mariners vs Bears	Toledo	Sunday	4:00
Chiefs vs Raptors	Cleveland	Monday	7:30

1. What night of the week does the Saints play?
2. What team does the Glaciers play against?
3. What rink will the Jays play ?
4. Mr. Collins drives the bus for the teams, what night of the week will be have to work in order to drive the team to the Buffalo Rink?
5. Which games starts before 5:00?
6. What game(s) are played on Sunday?

Pack Your Bags

Use the ticket below to answer the following questions

| TRANSAIR DL31 | Yao, Kimberly | A12 | TRANS AIR D31 |

PASSENGER
Yao, Kimberly

PASSENGER
Yao, Kimberly

GATE
A22

DEPARTURE
3:15 PM 15 DEC 2010

BOARDING ZONE
D3

SEAT
24C

DEPARTURE
3:15

TRACKING
2 207 365 3958 3309 0

DATA
00 I78 D

OPTIONS
1ST CL

OPTIONS
1ST CL

TRANSAIR

TRANSAIR

1. What is the boarding gate? _____
2. What is the departure time ? _____
3. What is the name of the airline? _____
4. What is the boarding zone? _____
5. What is the assigned seat? _____

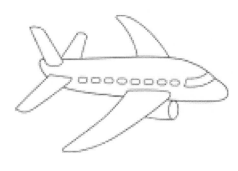

BLT

Using the following information, answer the questions below

- Ingredients
- Bacon
- Lettuce
- Tomato
- Bread (2 slices)
- mayonnaise
- Directions

- Place 2-3 strips bacon in a frying pan. Place the heat on medium and allow to fry for 10-15 minutes or until thoroughly cooked. While waiting for the bacon to cook, wash in cold water the lettuce and tomato. Once both are dry slice tomato and use 1-2 leaves of lettuce for sandwich.

- Place bread in the toaster and once toasted ,top with mayonnaise. Put the sandwich together tomatoes on the mayonnaise, lettuce on the tomatoes, and bacon on the lettuce. Add the second piece of bread.

1. What are the 5 ingredients to make the sandwich?
2. Are eggs part of the recipes?
3. How many slices of bread are needed to make this sandwich?
4. How many strips of bacon are needed ?
5. What do you need to do before assembling the sandwich?

Work Problems
Read and solve each word problem. Show your work

James groceries total $15.67. He gives he cashier $20.00. How much will he get back?

Mary has 3 packs of cigarettes. Each pack has 20 cigarettes. How many cigarettes does Mary have?

Ms. Button bought 3 dozen eggs from the grocery store. How many eggs has she have?

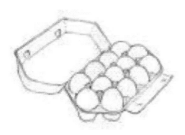

Word Problems

Read and solve each word problem. Show your work

In a nursing home there are 430 residents. 210 are females, how many are male?

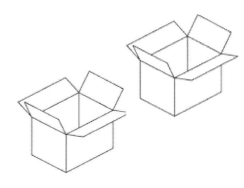

Steve's boss tells him he must pack 20 boxes every 30 minutes. How many boxes must he pack in 2 hours

Josiah sold 20 chocolate candy bars for $1.50 each. How much money did he make?

Word problems

Read and solve each word problem. Show your work

Last year there were 5225 slices of pizza served at the local pizzeria. This year the pizzeria wanted to serve more chicken wings so only 2342 slices of pizza were sold. What was the total number of slices of pizza served in the last two years?

Mr. Jones has $200 deducted from his pay check twice a month. How much will he have saved up in 3 months?

Sarah has $5,000 in her saving account. She spent $300 on shoes, $500 on a ticket to Hawaii, and $100 on a bathing suit. How much did she spent. How much many does she have left in he savings?

Camp Wilderness

Read and solve each word problem. Show your work

1. The Joanna' family is going on a camping trip this weekend. Both of her parents, her 2 brothers, 4 sisters and 2 grandparents are going on the trip. How many people are going including Joanna?

2. Joanna's arrives at the campground and realizes that they she forgot her fishing pole and bait. The nearest bait shop is 1and half miles down the road. Once she gets to the shop the fishing poles are $22.95, worms are $3.00/dozen. Joanna buys 2 dozen worms and 1 fishing pole.

    1. How much did Joanna spend?
    2. How many worms did Joanna buy total?
    3. How many total miles did Joanna go?

Saint Christopher's Church Annual Bake Sale

Read and solve each word problem. Show your work

1. Saint Christopher's church is holding it's annual bake sale. Sarah delivered 25 sweet potatoes pies, Macy delivered 15 blueberry and 10 chocolate pies.

    1. How many pies were there total

    2. If Mr. Brown brought all of the chocolate pies, how pies were left?

2. During the same time as the bake sale there is a rummage sale where attendees can pay $5 and fill a bag of miscellaneous items. While shopping, Cathy finds 2 end tables at $10 a piece and fills 3 bags of clothing. How much does Cathy owe?

Snack Shop

Use the menu below to answer the following questions

Potato Chips........75
Pretzel...............50
Popcorn..............55
Peanuts..............50
Bagels..............$1.25
Petite sandwiches...$2.25
Soup...............$1.75
Pizza slice..........$1.75

Cookies...................... .75
Donuts......................... $1.25
Ice cream cone.............$2.25
Milkshake......................$2.75
Chocolate Bar...............$1.00
Soda............................$1.25
Coffee.........................$2.25

1. Which snack cost the most?
2. Joe orders a slice of pizza, a soda and popcorn. How much did he spend?
3. Robin buys a cup of coffee and a candy bar. What was the total
4. Which snack cost the least?
5. Mike buys a milkshake, He gives the cashier $5.00, how much change does he get back?

Logic /Reasoning

Lets Go to The Zoo

Use the map below to answer the following questions

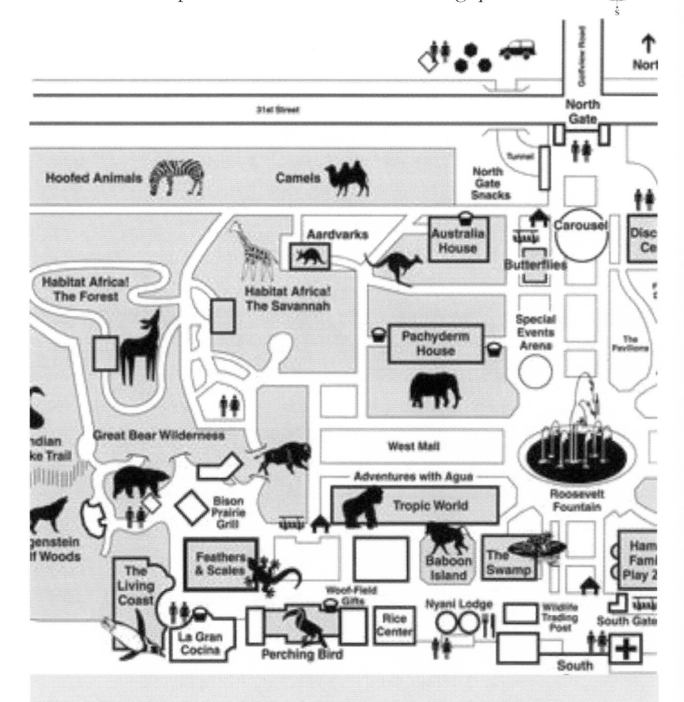

1. In what the north gate
2. Where is the first aid station located?
3. What is the name of the restaurant located in the zoo?

The Seasons

Use logical reasoning to solve the problem

	Rob	Tiffany	Mattie	Tammy
Summer				
Winter				
Spring				
Fall				

- Mattie Enjoys skiing
- Tammy does not like the four seasons
- Rob is allergic to the mold from the foliage

The Race

Use logical reasoning to solve the problem

	Brittany	Tiffany	Marcy	Tara
First Place				
Second Place				
Third Place				
Fourth Place				

- Tiffany did not finish first or last
- Tara ran faster than Marcy
- Brittany finished the race 2nd

Going Fishing

Use logical reasoning to solve the problem.

Five brothers went fishing while on a camping trip. Jesse, James, Jacob, Jimmie, and John each caught one fish. Read the clues, then use them to determine each brothers catch.

Trout 33 in

Walleye 22in

Salmon 36in

- Jesse's fish is larger than John's fish
- Jacob's fish is 3 inches longer than Jimmie's fish
- The length of James fish is not a multiple of 2
- Jimmie did not catch the smallest fish

Bass 18in

Who caught which fish

Jesse_____
Jacob_____
James_____
Jimmie_____
John_____

Catfish 23 in

Who wants Ice Cream?

Use the information provided below to determine fill in the missing data.

	Vanilla	Chocolate	Strawberry	Cookies & Crème
Sarah				
Rachael				
Julia				
Deborah				

1. Rachel's favorite ice cream is either strawberry or chocolate
2. Sarah does not like vanilla ice cream
3. Deborah's favorite is either Cookies and cream or Vanilla
4. Julia's favorite ice cream starts with the letter c

How Old am I?

Use the information provided below to determine fill in the missing data.

	30	31	32	33	34
Sarah					
Rachael					
Julia					
Deborah					
Kia					

1. Sarah's age is a odd number
2. Rachel and Julia are one year apart
3. Rachel is the oldest
4. Kia is younger than Deborah

I love Jewels

Use the information provided below to determine fill in the missing data.

	Gold	Silver	Diamond	Ruby	Pearl
Sarah					
Caitlin					
Gina					
Tina					
Robin					

1. Sarah does not like gold or Pearls
2. Robin has jewelry that starts with the first letter of her name
3. Tina's great aunt gave her diamond earrings for Christmas last year
4. Gina likes silver or gold jewelry

What Day is it?

Use the calendar below to answer the following questions

Sunday	Monday	Tuesday	Wednesday	Thursday	Friday	Saturday
		1	2	3	4	5
6	7	8	9	10	11	12
13	14	15	16	17	18	19
20	21	22	23	24	25	26
27	28	29	30	31		

1. Work begins one week after the second Sunday. Mark that date with a blue marker
2. The basketball game comes on the third Thursday. Place a x on that date.
3. The doctors appointment is three weeks before the fifth Tuesday. Mark with date with a red marker
4. What date is 9 days after the third Wednesday? Mark that date with a green marker
5. The picnic is the day after the 4th Friday. Mark that date with a black marker

Patterns Everywhere!

Continue the pattern below

235, 233, 231

4, 8, 12, 16......

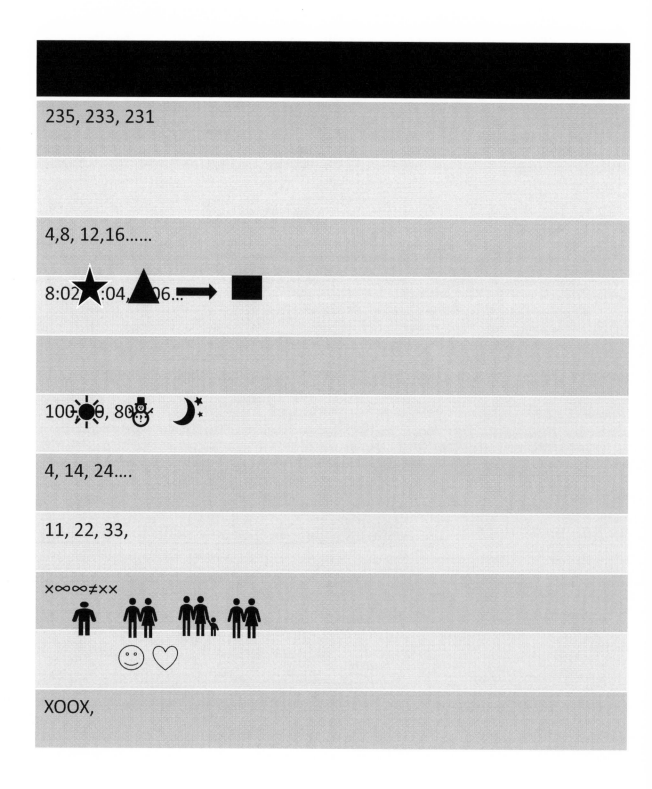

8:02 ★ :04, ▲ :06... ➡ ■

100, ☀ 0, 80 ⛄ 🌙

4, 14, 24....

11, 22, 33,

x∞∞≠xx

XOOX,

Logic
Identify which item does not belong n each row

Logic

Identify which item does not belong n each row

Logic
Identify which item does not belong n each row

Logic

Identify which item does not belong n each row

Logic

Identify which item does not belong n each row

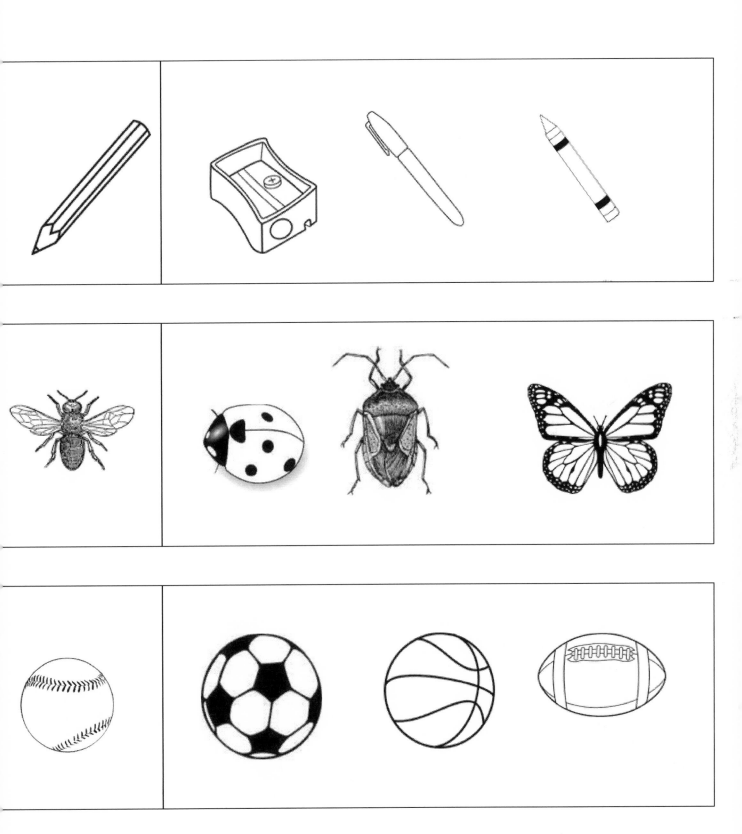

Follow the directions listed below

- Draw **a Red** around the animals
- Draw a **Blue X** on the things with wheels
- Draw a **Green** on the things you wear
- Draw and **Yellow** around things you eat

We Go together
Draw a line between the objects that go together

Answer Key

Counting
Fill in the missing number

1	2	3	4	5	6	7	8	9	10
11	12	13	14	15	16	17	18	19	20
21	22	23	24	25	26	27	28	29	30
31	32	33	34	35	36	37	38	39	40
41	42	43	44	45	46	47	48	49	50
51	52	53	54	55	56	57	58	59	60
61	62	63	64	65	66	67	68	69	70
71	72	73	74	75	76	77	78	79	80

All kind of Shapes
Identify each shape by marking the name next to it

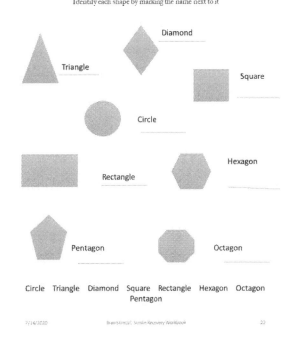

Triangle

Diamond

Square

Circle

Rectangle

Hexagon

Pentagon

Octagon

Circle   Triangle   Diamond   Square   Rectangle   Hexagon   Octagon   Pentagon

More Shapes
Identify each shape by coloring all triangles red and all squares yellow.

Music in the Air
Match the instruments on the left with the instruments on the right

Transportation

Match the items on the left column with the item on the right

Matching

Match the items on the left column with the item on the right

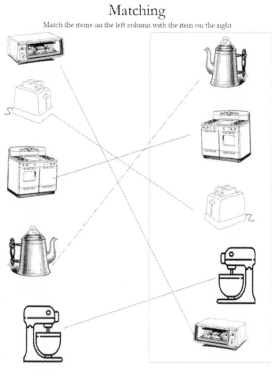

Matching

Match each object to the highlighted word

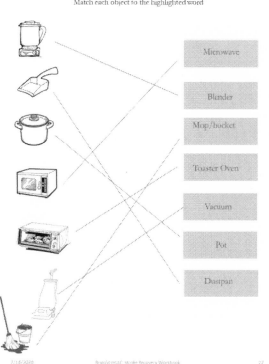

Microwave

Blender

Mop/bucket

Toaster Oven

Vacuum

Pot

Dustpan

Clothing

Match each object to the word highlighted in the middle.

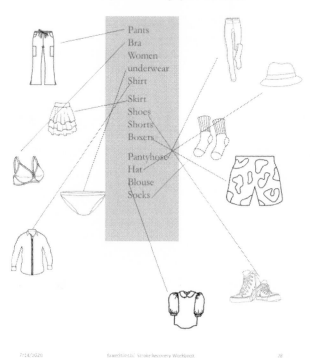

Pants
Bra
Women
underwear
Shirt
Skirt
Shoes
Shorts
Boxers
Pantyhose
Hat
Blouse
Socks

Kitchen Items
Read each word and match the word with the object below

Pan   Cup   Pot

Bowl   Spoon   Sink

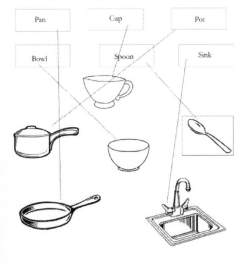

Let's Have a Picnic
Read each word and match the word with the object below

Wine   Cheese   Pie   Corn

Hotdogs   Grapes   Sandwich

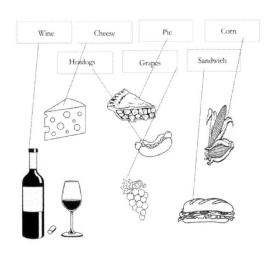

Matching
Match each animal with their home

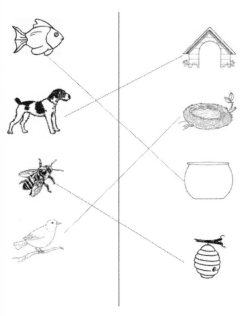

Matching
Draw at line from the item on the left to the item on the right with at direct relationship

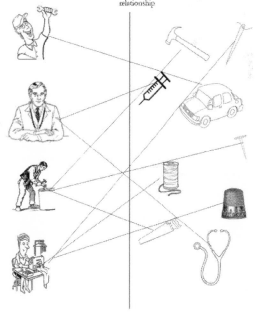

Origins

Draw at line from the item on the left to the item on the right with at direct relationship

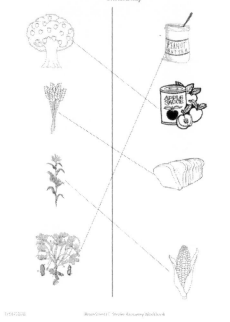

What are you eating?

Pair each animal with the foods that they eat

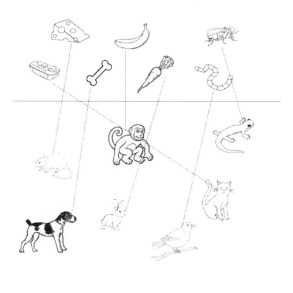

Can you Find the Differences?

Find the item that is different in each group

Can you Find the Differences?

Find the item that is different in each group

Day and Night

What Can you see during the Day?

What Can you see during the Night?

Moon   Clouds   Birds   Bats   Sun   Stars

It's Cold Outside

Which Of these items does not represent winter

Emotions

Pair the emotion from the word to the correct emotion in the picture

Excited   Angry   Happy   Sad   Bored   Scared

The Holidays

Identify each holiday using the words in the key below

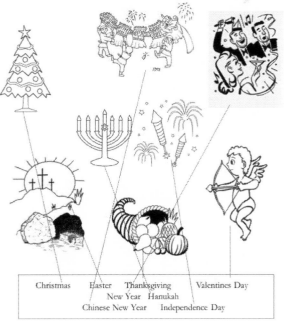

Christmas   Easter   Thanksgiving   Valentines Day
New Year   Hanukah
Chinese New Year   Independence Day

Who Are We?
Match the pictures with the respective names below

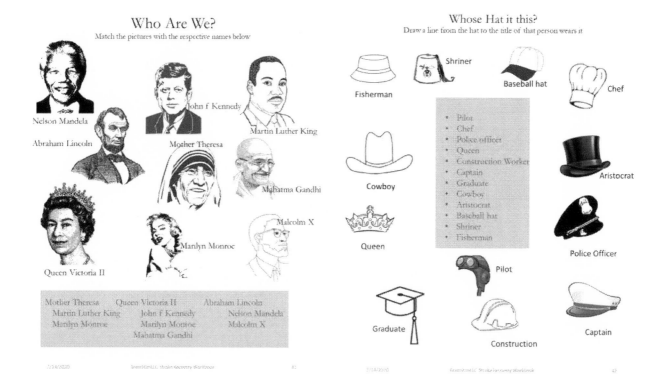

Nelson Mandela
John f Kennedy
Abraham Lincoln
Mother Theresa
Martin Luther King
Mahatma Gandhi
Malcolm X
Marilyn Monroe
Queen Victoria II

Mother Theresa	Queen Victoria II	Abraham Lincoln
Martin Luther King	John f Kennedy	Nelson Mandela
Marilyn Monroe	Marilyn Monroe	Malcolm X
	Mahatma Gandhi	

Whose Hat it this?
Draw a line from the hat to the title of that person wears it

Fisherman
Shriner
Baseball hat
Chef
Cowboy
Aristocrat
Queen
Police Officer
Pilot
Graduate
Construction
Captain

- Pilot
- Chef
- Police officer
- Queen
- Construction Worker
- Captain
- Graduate
- Cowboy
- Aristocrat
- Baseball hat
- Shriner
- Fisherman

Planes Trains Automobiles
Answer the following using the pictures below

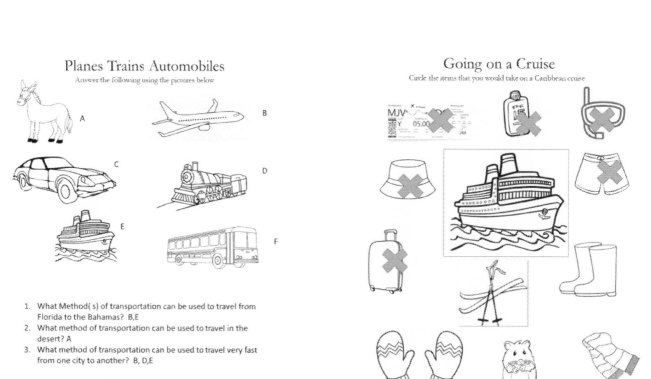

A
B
C
D
E
F

1. What Method(s) of transportation can be used to travel from Florida to the Bahamas? B,E
2. What method of transportation can be used to travel in the desert? A
3. What method of transportation can be used to travel very fast from one city to another? B, D,E

Going on a Cruise
Circle the items that you would take on a Caribbean cruise

Hygiene

Discuss how each of these objects are used

1.   Used to take a bath
2.   Used to clean body
3.   Used to clean teeth
4.   Used to soften skin to shave
5.   Used to assist with shaving, cut hair
6.   Used to assist with sweating
7.   Used with shaving lather
8.   Used to moisture skin
9.   Used to trim the nail

Hygiene

Draw a line from the object on the left to the matching number of item(s) on the right

It's Raining

Identify by circling the items that should be worn in the rain

Relationships

Pair the objects on the right with the objects in the left column

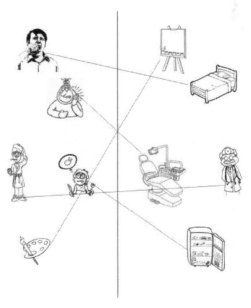

Spring Has Sprung
Circle the images that best represent spring

Sports
Using the Balls below, draw a line to the equipment that best represent each sport

Sports
Using the Balls below, draw a line to the equipment that best represent each sport

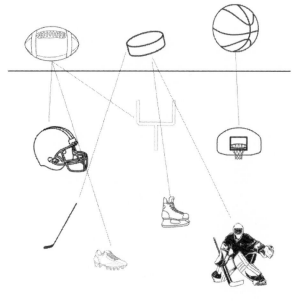

Counting Exercise
Draw a line from the box to the matching number of items

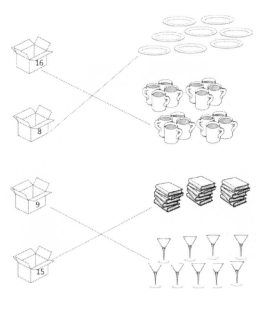

Counting Exercise
Draw a line from the box to the matching number of items

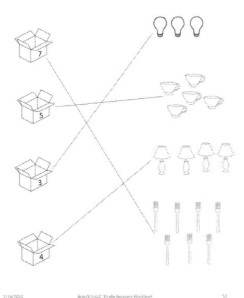

Measurement
Number each item from the shortest (1) to the longest (5)

2 ___

1 ___

5 ___

3 ___

4 ___

The Ruler
Cut out the ruler at the bottom of the page . Use it to measure the length in centimeters of each object.

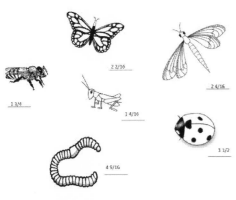

2 2/16

2 4/16

1 3/4

1 4/16

1 1/2

4 9/16

The Ruler
Cut out the ruler at the bottom of the page . Use it to measure the length in inches of each object.

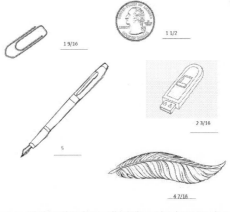

1 9/16

1 1/2

2 3/16

5

4 7/16

Broken Clock
Please help us fix the clock by filling in the missing numbers

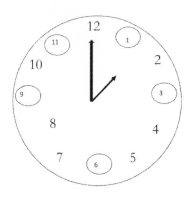

What Time is it?
Write the time below of each clock

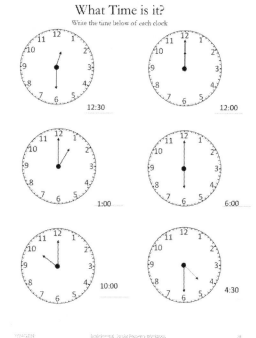

12:30

12:00

1:00

6:00

10:00

4:30

What Time is It?
Draw Hands according to the appropriate time

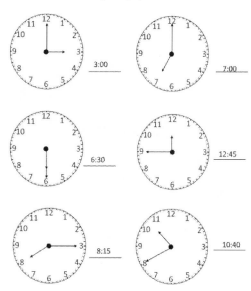

3:00

7:00

6:30

12:45

8:15

10:40

What time is it?
Write the time below of each clock

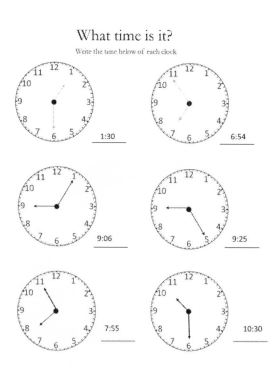

1:30

6:54

9:06

9:25

7:55

10:30

What time is it?
Write the time on the line below each clock

 Seventeen minutes past ten O'clock

10:17

 Thirty-three minutes past six O'clock

6:33

 Noon

12:00

 Fifteen minutes to one O'clock

1:15

Show Me the Money!
Write the money value on the line provided

1¢   5¢   10¢   25¢

$1.00

Show me the Money
Write the money value.

 5¢

 10¢

 50¢

 75¢

Pick the Right Price
Read the price on each vase. Draw a line to the money you need to buy it.

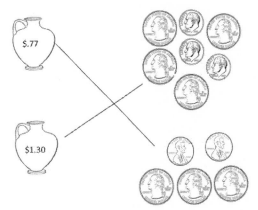

$.85

$.77

$1.30

Pick the Right Price

Read the price on each vase. Draw a line to the money you need to buy it.

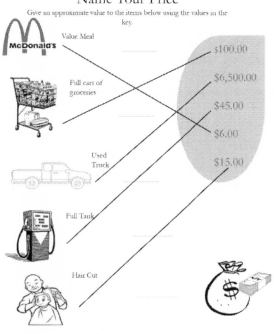

Name Your Price

Give an approximate value to the items below using the values in the key.

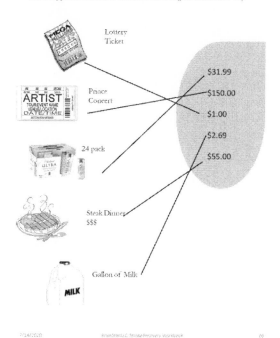

Lottery Ticket

Prince Concert

24 pack

Steak Dinner $$$

Gallon of Milk

$31.99
$150.00
$1.00
$2.69
$55.00

Name Your Price

Give an approximate value to the items below using the values in the key.

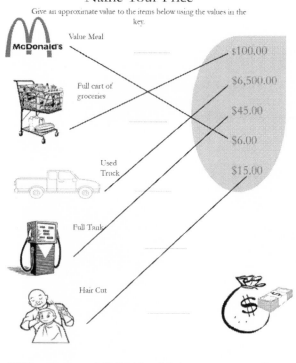

Value Meal

Full cart of groceries

Used Truck

Full Tank

Hair Cut

$100.00
$6,500.00
$45.00
$6.00
$15.00

Name Your Price

Give an approximate value to the items below using the values in the key.

Value Meal

Full cart of groceries

Used Truck

Full Tank

Hair Cut

$100,00
$6,500.00
$45.00
$6.00
$15.00

Behind
Circle the objects that are behind

On Top
Circle the objects that are on top

Under
Circle all of the items that under

Signs
Identify the appropriate signs using the phrases below

- Merge to the right
- Two way traffic
- Means to Halt
- Speed limit to not exceed 45mph
- No trucks allow
- Slippery driving
- Do not Enter
- Give the right away
- Crossroad ahead

Signs

Identify the appropriate signs using the phrases below

- Men's bathroom
- No smoking area
- Family restroom
- No cell phones Allowed
- Please Recycle
- Family bathroom
- Steep, watch step
- This way out
- Slippery

Signs

Identify the appropriate signs using the phrases below

Hotel	School	Hospital	Airport	Bus
Playground	Gas Station	Food	Parking	No Parking
Women Rest Room		Camping		

Safety

Identify the appropriate signs using the phrases below

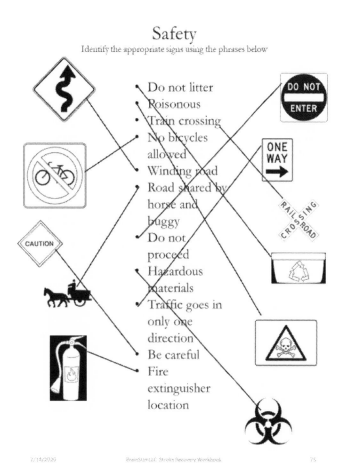

- Do not litter
- Poisonous
- Train crossing
- No bicycles allowed
- Winding road
- Road shared by horse and buggy
- Do not proceed
- Hazardous materials
- Traffic goes in only one direction
- Be careful
- Fire extinguisher location

What's in Your Refrigerator

Circle the item(s) that belong in the refrigerator?

What's in the Wash

Circle all of the items that do not belong in the washing machine

Make a Egg Sequencing

Number 1-5 the order of operation beginning at what happened first

Planting Sequencing

Number 1-5 the order of operation beginning at what happened first

Folder Sorting

Read each word and place in the appropriate folder

Shirt	Grapes	Black	Green
Apple	Sock	Blouse	Banana
Orange	Blue	Purple	Nightgown
Pants	Avocado	Pineapple	White
Red	Watermelon	Mulberry	Stocking
Tie	Bra	Skirt	Camisole

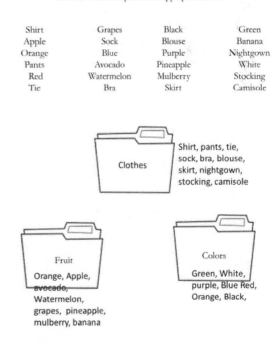

Clothes

Shirt, pants, tie, sock, bra, blouse, skirt, nightgown, stocking, camisole

Fruit

Orange, Apple, avocado, Watermelon, grapes, pineapple, mulberry, banana

Colors

Green, White, purple, Blue Red, Orange, Black,

Recycle

Place items in the appropriate recycling bin

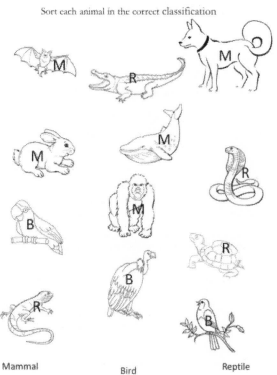

Folder Sorting

Read each word and place in the appropriate folder

Tire	August	Thursday	Bed
Monday	Friday	Chair	June
Sad	Happy	Rug	Wednesday
Depressed	Muffler	Brakes	Angry
Steering	July	Motor	Stressed
wheel	Wiper	September	Frustrated
February	Saturday	Sunday	Television

Sad, Depressed, Happy, angry, Stressed, frustrated — **Feelings**

Monday, Friday, Saturday, Thursday, Sunday, Wednesday, — **Days of the Week**

February, August, July, September, June — **Months**

Tire, steering wheel, muffler, wiper, brakes, motor, — **Car Parts**

House Items — Chair, rug, bed, television

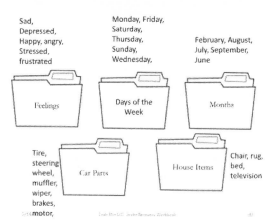

What am I?

Sort each animal in the correct classification

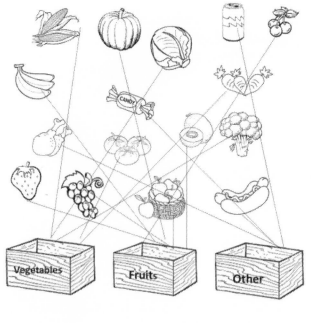

Mammal   Bird   Reptile

What am I?

Sort each item in the correct classification

Vegetables   Fruits   Other

Sequence Writing

Using the pictures below identify each step of the task of washing clothes Write each step below

Let's do the Laundry

1. First I am going to __Sort Clothes__
2. Next, I am going to __Turn on the washing machine__
3. Next I am going to __Add Laundry detergent__
4. Next I am going to __Put clothes in the machine__
5. Next, I am going to __Place clothes in the dryer 45-50__
6. Last, I am going to __Fold the clothes__

- Sort clothes
- Add laundry detergent
- Put clothes in the machine
- Place clothes in dryer 45-50 minutes
- Turn on washing machine
- Fold clothes

Sequence Writing

Identify each step of making a cake using the key below. Write each step on the lines provided

Let's bake a cake

Ingredients
1. Eggs
2. Margarine/Oil
3. Water
4. Cake Mix

Prep
1. Heat oven 350
2. Empty content into a bowl
3. Mix all ingredients together
4. Pour mixed batter into cake pan

Bake
1. Place in the oven for 35-40 minutes
2. _____

Cooling
1. Let cool for 15minutes
2. Icing cake
3. _____

• Eggs	• Mix all ingredients together	• Icing cake
• Margarine/oil	• Pour mixed batter into a cake pan	• Let cool for 10-15 minutes
• Water		• Flour
• Empty content into a bowl	• Place in oven of 35-40 minutes	• Heat oven to 350°

Music Everywhere

Read each statement and use to identify the musical instrument

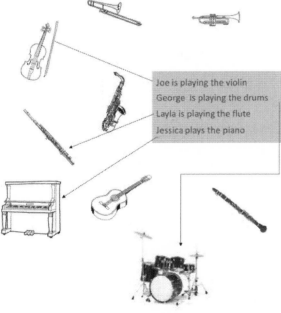

Joe is playing the violin
George is playing the drums
Layla is playing the flute
Jessica plays the piano

Measurements

Answer the questions about the liquid volume. Show your work

1 gallon=4 Quarts   1Quart= 2 pints   1Pint=2 Cups   1Cup=8 Ounces

Stephen drank 1 pint of coffee for lunch. How many cups of coffee did he drink? __2 cups__

Sarah started her morning water intake with a gallon of water; divided into four parts. How much does each container hold? __4 Quarts__

Ezra added a half cup of butter to the brownie mixture, how many ounces did he add __4 ounces__

Mrs. Wells, brought 2 quarts of orange juice at the market, how many cups will she have to give to her children? __4 cups__

Inferences

Inferences is a Conclusion reached based on evidence and reasoning.

What inference can be drawn from the following statements?

Josiah is very happy after unwrapping his birthday gift.

There are muddy paw prints on the new carpet.

Josiah liked his gift/ He was happy with his gift

A animal tracked mud into the new carpet

Inferences

Inferences is a Conclusion reached based on evidence and reasoning.

What inference can be drawn from the following statements?

1.

Sarah left a several shopping bags on the floor in the house and is walking around in her new dress

2.

Stephen see a milk puddle next to the refrigerator and see Josiah with a milk mustache

1. Sarah went shopping, Sarah was excited about her new dress

2. Josiah spilled the milk on the floor

Inferences

Inferences is a Conclusion reached based on evidence and reasoning.

What inference can be drawn from the following statements?

1.

Mr. Johnston is extremely excited and jumping up and down shouting "hoo-ray" while holding his lottery ticket .

2.

James walked into the grocery with mud all over his boots.

1. Mr. Johnson won the lotto/ He has a winning ticket

2. James was in a muddy area/ worked in a muddy area

Inferences

Inferences is a Conclusion reached based on evidence and reasoning.

What inference can be drawn from the following statements?

1.

Mr. Parker is seen leaving the hospital in a wheelchair with a cast on his leg

2.

Ms. Jones Looked inside the desk, under the bed and on top of the refrigerator for the keys

1. Mr. Parker injured/ broke his leg

2. Ms. Jones lost her keys

Over the last 3 months, the member of St Christopher's church has been collecting items to be recycled. The graph below represents each recycled item that was turned in.

Saint Christopher's Recycling Fundraising Dive

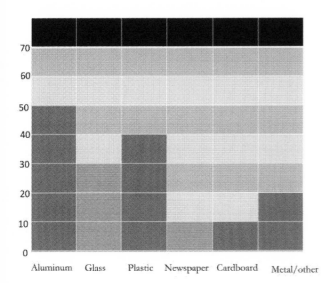

Aluminum Glass Plastic Newspaper Cardboard Metal/other

Using the graph on the previous page to answer questions below.

1. How many aluminum and glass items were recycled 80
2. How many more plastic items were recycled then metal/other? ...20
3. Which recycled item was brought in the most?.. Aluminum
4. What was the total number of glass and plastic? ...70
5. If this fundraiser went on for 3 more month, estimate how much cardboard would have been recycled? ...40
6. If this fundraiser went on for 3 more month, estimate how much glass an aluminum would have been recycled? ...320

Read the excerpt of the article and answer the questions

Vaping Can Be Addictive Panel Concludes and May Lure Teenagers to Smoking, Science

Jan.23.2018

WASHINGTON — A national panel of public health experts concluded in a report released on Tuesday that vaping with e-cigarettes that contain nicotine can be addictive and that teenagers who use the devices may be at higher risk of smoking.

Whether teenage use of e-cigarettes leads to conventional smoking has been intensely debated in the United States and elsewhere. While the industry argues that vaping is not a steppingstone to conventional cigarettes or addiction, some antismoking advocates contend that young people become hooked on nicotine, and are enticed to use cancer-causing tobacco-based cigarettes over time.

1. Who is this article about? Teenagers
2. What is this article about? Vaping is addictive and entices Teens to smoke
3. When did this article come out? January 23, 2018
4. Where is this happening? U.S and throughout the world
5. Why is this happening? Teens are becoming addicted to the nicotine
6. How are youth becoming hooked on nicotine? Nicotine is in an ingredient in vaping devices

Read the excerpt of the article and answer the questions

Australia weather: Monsoon rains cause floods in Queensland

Feb 2, 2019

Exceptional monsoon rains have caused severe flooding in parts of Australia's north-eastern state of Queensland.

Cars and livestock have been swept away over a large area around the coastal city of Townsville. Emergency crews are evacuating people on rafts.

Up to 20,000 homes could be flooded if the downpours continue, officials warn.

A dam has reached twice its capacity and water is being released to avoid putting further strain on it. More rain is expected in the coming days.

Northern Queensland has a tropical climate and experiences monsoon rain from December to April. But the current conditions in the Townsville area are rare.

"We have not been in this situation before," Queensland Premier Annastacia Palaszczuk is quoted as saying by the Australian Broadcasting Corporation (ABC).

"There has been a lot of rain falling over the Townsville catchment and some of these levels are unprecedented."

Who is Queensland Premier? Annastacia Palaszczuk
What is happening in this article ? Severe flooding caused by monsoons
When did this event take place? February 2,2019
How many homes could be affected ? 20,000
How is the city dealing with this crisis? Releasing water from the dam
Why is the city flooding? Queensland tropical climate causing monsoons

Opposites
Draw a line to the object representing the opposite

Opposites
Draw a line to the object representing the opposite

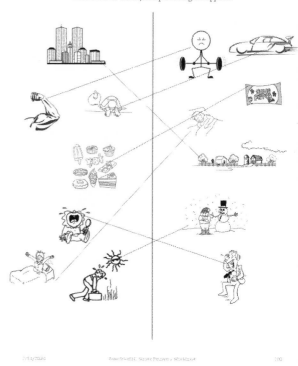

Antonym
Find the word that means the opposite of

Light	Depressed
alike	Dark
Happy	Exit
Bottom	Top
Entrance	Exterior
Interior	Smooth
Rough	speechless
Communicate	Different

Antonym
Find the word that means the opposite of

Cowardly	Unsteady
Vanish	Brave
Private	Appear
Faithful	Public
Forward	Shy
Loyal	Arrogant
Humble	Unreliable
Sleep	Awake

Draw a line to the words that describes the word in the middle

Draw a line to the words that describes the word in the middle

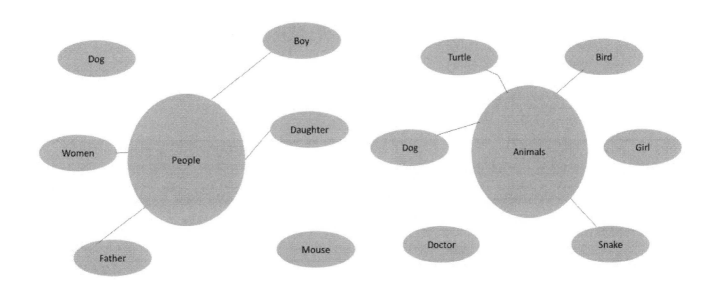

Synonyms
Draw a line to the words that describes the word in the middle

Just

Fair

Authentic

Ethical

Frank

Honest

Lying

Partial

Genuine

Synonyms
Draw a line to the words that describes the word in the middle

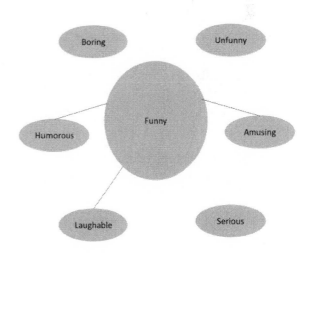

Synonyms
Find the word that means the same

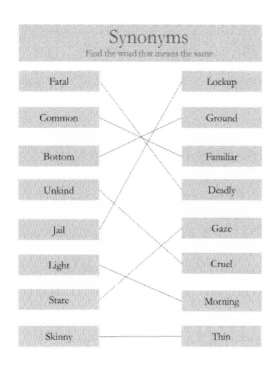

Fatal	Lockup
Common	Ground
Bottom	Familiar
Unkind	Deadly
Jail	Gaze
Light	Cruel
Stare	Morning
Skinny	Thin

Describe This!
Give a brief definition/description of the following terms

Duck	Quacks, swims in water can fly, webbed feet, lay eggs
Goat	Curved backward horns, used for milk meat
Dog	4 legs, barks, has a tail,
Cat	Meows , 4 legs, chases mice, has whiskers, fur.
Bowl	Round dish, curved, good for serving food, soup
Spoon	Utensil used to eat soups cereals,
Hat	Head covering, protects the head
Cheese	Dairy product, yellowish orange, made from milk,
Apple	Red/ yellow/green , round, different types, has seeds in the middle,
Pie	Round, made with different fruits, has a crust

Describe This!
Give a brief definition/description of the following terms

Above	Over, can't touch, higher
Again	To repeat, another time, once more
Mr. /Mrs	Married, surname
Give	To hand over, to freely transfer a possession, to allow
Funny	Humorous, causes you to laugh, amusing
House	Place to live, a building that provides shelter
Yours	Ownership, belongs to you
Wash	To clean, to cleanse, to rinse, to lather
Think	To have a opinion, belief, idea, own minds idea
Sorry	To apologize, to feel remorseful, to regret, to distress, sympathy

Describe This!
Give a brief definition/description of the following terms

Harvest	To gather, In medicine to remove cells for transplantation
Refund	To give or put back, to return
Ignore	Refuse to notice or acknowledge, fail to consider
Concentrate	To focus, put forth mental effort, to gather people
Reject	To dismiss as inadequate,
debate	To argue, to talk, in a formal manner
Renew	To make new again, reestablish , to repeat ,to resume after interruption
Generous	Giving, showing kindness, plentiful
Celebrate	To honor, commemorate, salute, recognize,
Competition	Contest, opposition, competitiveness

Describe This!
Give a brief definition/description of the following terms

Yesterday	The past, the other day, the day before today
Edge	The outside limit of a object, furthest away from the center
Travel	Journey, tour, voyage roam, trek
Opinion	Own personal thoughts, personal belief, judgement,
Compare	Similar between two objects
Emphasize	To give importance to, press stress on,
Carefully	To be cautious, avoiding potential dangers
Instrument	A tool used to produce a sound, to exploit, a device
Region	An area , district, territory
Persuade	To cause to do something through reasoning, to convince, make, talk someone into

Describe This!
Give a brief definition/description of the following terms

Within	Inside something, in a area or boundary
Large	Relatively great size, big, huge, gigantic
Follow	To go after, to travel behind, to come after
Before	Preceding, in front of
Under	Below, beneath, inferior, subordinate
Important	Great value, significant
Soon	In a short time, happening in the near future
Later	In the present, after a while,
Understand	To comprehend, able to interpret, to perceive
Between	Separating two things, into,

Fact and Opinion
Read each statement. Place a X if the statement is a fact or a opinion

Statement		Fact	Opinion
A bicycle has two wheels	F		
Dog is a man's best friend	O		
Albany is the capital of New York	F		
Nobody likes pinto beans	O		
Debate is another word for talk	F		
A group of birds is called a flock	F		
Canada is north of the United States	F		
The Buffalo Bills are awesome	O		
Plants need water in order to grow	F		
Apples are the best fruit	O		
Barack Obama is the 44th president of the United States	F		
The earth is round	F		
Florida is the best state	O		

Fact versus Non-Fiction
Read each statement. Place a X on the respective line
HINT** non-fiction -- (real events, real people)

	Statement		Fiction	Non-Fiction
1.	Little Red Riding Hood	F		
2.	The autobiography of George Washington	NF		
3.	An article about how to grow a garden	NF		
4.	A football trade card with stats on the back	NF		
5.	Introduction to Biology	NF		
6.	The Prince of Niccolò Machiavelli	NF		
7.	Alice and Wonderland	F		
8.	Diary of Anne Frank	NF		
9.	Hamlet	F		
10.	Cartoons in the newspaper	F		
11.	A short story	F		
12.	The assignation of John F Kennedy	NF		

Compare and Contrast
Read the paragraph and then compare and contrast in the diagram below

Similarities   Differences

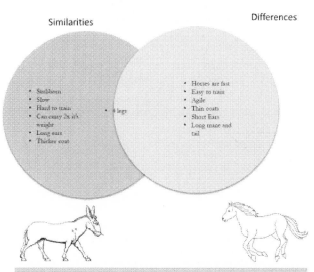

- Stubborn
- Slow
- Hard to train
- Can carry 2x it's weight
- Long ears
- Thicker coat

4 legs

- Horses are fast
- Easy to train
- Agile
- Thin coats
- Short Ears
- Long mane and tail

Horses and Donkey are not very similar. Although they both have four legs and evolve from the Equidae, they have a lot of differences. For instance horses are fast, easy to train and agile. They have a thin coats, short ears and long manes and tails . Donkeys on the other hand are intelligent but harder to train, able to carry 2x their weight, they have thicker coats, shorter tails, and long ears.

Compare and Contrast
Read the paragraph and then compare and contrast in the diagram below

- Domesticated
- Shorter legs than wolves
- Eat kibble

- 4 legs
- related family
- Animals
- Fur
- Run in packs

- Larger head than dog
- Big paws
- Eye color amber yellow
- White/black or grey fur

Wolves and Dogs have many things in common. They both have animals that live all over the world. Another similarity is that the both have four legs, and both have fur. Wolves like dogs do for packs but only wolves hunt in packs. Both wolf and dogs can liv outdoors, but dogs are domesticated and can live in doors as well. Finally, wolves are primarily carnivores.

Answer the questions using the graph below

SURVEY ON FAVORITE VEGETABLES
Elderberry Skilled Nursing Home

Peas 9.7%
Brussel sprouts 10%
Green Beans 23%
Broccoli 58%

1. This pie chart gives data about what?   Survey of Favorite vegetables
2. The second largest section of the graph represents what?   Green Beans
3. What percentage of the patients like green beans?   23%
4. Almost 10% of the patients like what vegetable?   Peas
5. What percentage of the populations would like peas and brussels sprouts?

Using the graph below answer the questions

Buffalo Winter Driving
Car Accidents

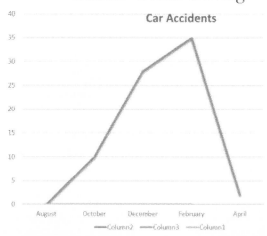

Column2   Column3   Column1

1. The line graphs represents the relationship between what two things? **Weather and Driving Accidents**
2. How many accidents did Buffalo have in the month of October?
3. As the weather got colder in December where there more or less accidents? **More**
4. What happened in April as the weather got warmer? **Accidents declined**

Tables of Contents
Answer the questions using the table of contents

1. On which page can you find the recipe for pecan waffles? **19**
2. What page should to turn to for more information about fritters **21**
3. If you are looking for direction on how to make biscuits, which page should you read? **31**
4. If you are interested in learning more about cooking which page should you read? **2**
5. What does it talk about on page 25? **Bread Rolls**

Hockey Playoff Schedule
Answer the questions using the hockey play off schedule

TEAMS	RINK	DATE	TIMES
Sabers vs. Eagles	Buffalo	Sunday	1:00
Giants vs Jays	Akron	Wednesday	7:30
Bulls vs Saints	Ontario	Saturday	7:00
Glaciers vs Reds	Buffalo	Friday	8:00
Mariners vs Bears	Toledo	Sunday	4:00
Chiefs vs Raptors	Cleveland	Monday	7:30

1. What night of the week does the Saints play? **Saturday**
2. What team does the Glaciers play against? **Reds**
3. What rink will the Jays play ? **Akron**
4. Mr. Collins drives the bus for the teams, what night of the week will be have to work in order to drive the team to the Buffalo Rink? **Friday and Sunday**
5. Which games starts before 5:00? **Sabers/Eagles, Mariners/Bears**
6. What game(s) are played on Sunday? **Sabers/Eagles, Mariners/Bears**

Pack Your Bags
Use the ticket below to answer the following questions

TRANSAIR DL31 Yao, Kimberly A12	TRANS AIR D31
PASSENGER Yao, Kimberly	PASSENGER Yao, Kimberly
GATE **A22** DEPARTURE **3:15** PM 15 DEC 2010 BOARDING ZONE **D3**	SEAT **24C** DEPARTURE **3:15**
TRACKING 2 207 365 3958 3300 0 SEATS 00 178 D OPTIONS 1ST CL	OPTIONS 1ST CL
TRANSAIR	TRANSAIR

1. What is the boarding gate? A22
2. What is the departure time ? 3:15pm
3. What is the name of the airline? TRANSAIR
4. What is the boarding zone? D3
5. What is the assigned seat ? 24C

BLT
Using the following information, answer the questions below

- Ingredients
- Bacon
- Lettuce
- Tomato
- Bread (2 slices)
- mayonnaise
- Directions
- Place 2-3 strips bacon in a frying pan. Place the heat on medium and allow to fry for 10-15 minutes or until thoroughly cooked. While waiting for the bacon to cook, wash in cold water the lettuce and tomato. Once both are dry slice tomato and use 1-2 leaves of lettuce for sandwich.
- Place bread in the toaster and once toasted, top with mayonnaise. Put the sandwich together tomatoes on the mayonnaise, lettuce on the tomatoes, and bacon on the lettuce. Add the second piece of bread.

1. What are the 5 ingredients to make the sandwich? …**Lettuce, Tomato, mayonnaise, bread bacon**
2. Are eggs part of the recipes? **No**
3. How many slices of bread are needed to make this sandwich? **2**
4. How many strips of bacon are needed ? **2-3**
5. What do you need to do before assembling the sandwich? **Toast bread**

Work Problems

Read and solve each word problem. Show your work

James groceries total $15.67. He gives the cashier $20.00. How much will he get back? **$4.33 left**

Mary has 3 packs of cigarettes. Each pack has 20 cigarettes. How many cigarettes does Mary have? **60 cigarettes**

Ms. Button bought 3 dozen eggs from the grocery store. How many eggs has she have? **36 Eggs**

Word Problems

Read and solve each word problem. Show your work

In a nursing home there are 430 residents. 210 are females, how many are male? **220 male residents**

Steve's boss tells him he must pack 20 boxes every 30 minutes. How many boxes must he pack in 2 hours **80 boxes**

Josiah sold 20 chocolate candy bars for $1.50 each. How much money did he make? **$30 dollars**

Word problems

Read and solve each word problem. Show your work

Last year there were 5225 slices of pizza served at the local pizzeria. This year the pizzeria wanted to serve more chicken wings so only 2342 slices of pizza were sold. What was the total number of slices of pizza served in the last two years?

Mr. Jones has $200 deducted from his pay check twice a month. How much will he have saved up in 3 months? **$1200 saved**

Sarah has $5,000 in her saving account. She spent $300 on shoes, $500 on a ticket to Hawaii, and $100 on a bathing suit. How much did she spent. How much many does she have left in he savings? **$4100 left**

Camp Wilderness

Read and solve each word problem. Show your work

1. The Joanna' family is going on a camping trip this weekend. Both of her parents, her 2 brothers, 4 sisters and 2 grandparents are going on the trip. How many people are going including Joanna?

11 family members

1. Joanna's arrives at the campground and realizes that they she forgot her fishing pole and bait. The nearest bair shop is 1and half miles down the road. Once she gets to the shop the fishing poles are $22.95, worms are $3.00/dozen. Joanna buys 2 dozen worms and 1 fishing pole.

$28.95

1. How much did Joanna spend?
2. How many worms did Joanna buy total? **24**
3. How many total miles did Joanna go? **3 miles total**

Saint Christopher's Church Annual Bake Sale

Read and solve each word problem. Show your work

1. Saint Christopher's church is holding it's annual bake sale. Sarah delivered 25 sweet potatoes pies, Macy delivered 15 blueberry and 10 chocolate pies.
    1. How many pies were there total **50 pies**
    2. If Mr. Brown brought all of the chocolate pies, how pies were left? **40 pies left**

2. During the same time as the bake sale there is a rummage sale where attendees can pay $5 and fill a bag of miscellaneous items. While shopping, Cathy finds 2 end tables at $10 a piece and fills 3 bags of clothing. How much does Cathy owe? **$35 total**

Snack Shop

Use the menu below to answer the following questions

Potato Chips........75	Cookies........................... .75
Pretzel................50	Donuts.........................$1.25
Popcorn................55	Ice cream cone............$2.25
Peanuts................50	Milkshake......................$2.75
Bagels...............$1.25	Chocolate Bar.............$1.00
Petite sandwiches...$2.25	Soda.............................$1.25
Soup.................$1.75	Coffee...........................$2.25
Pizza slice...........$1.75	

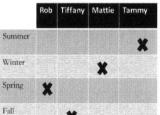

1.Which snack cost the most? **Milkshake**
2. Joe orders a slice of pizza, a soda and popcorn. How much did he spend? **$3.55**
3. Robin buys a cup of coffee and a candy bar. What was the total **$3.25**
4. Which snack cost the least? **Peanuts**
5. Mike buys a milkshake, He gives the cashier $5.00, how much change does he get back? **$2.25**

Lets Go to The Zoo

Use the map below to answer the following questions

1. In what direction is the carousel If am and standing the north gate **SOUTH**
2. Where is the first aid station located ? **Near South Gate**
3. What is the name of the restaurant located in the zoo? **Nyani Lodge**

The Seasons

Use logical reasoning to solve the problem

	Rob	Tiffany	Mattie	Tammy
Summer				X
Winter			X	
Spring	X			
Fall		X		

- Mattie Enjoys skiing
- Tammy does not like the four seasons
- Rob is allergic to the mold from the foliage

The Race

Use logical reasoning to solve the problem

	Brittany	Tiffany	Marcy	Tara
First Place				X
Second Place	X			
Third Place		X		
Fourth Place			X	

- Tiffany did not finish first or last
- Tara ran faster than Marcy
- Brittany finished the race 2nd

Going Fishing

Use logical reasoning to solve the problem.

Five brothers went fishing on a camping trip. Jesse, James, Jacob, Jimmie, and John each caught one fish. Read the clues, then use them to determine each brothers catch.

Trout 33 in

Walleye 22in

Salmon 36in

Bass 18in

- Jesse's fish is larger than John's fish
- Jacob's fish is 3 inches longer than Jimmie's fish
- The length of James fish is not a multiple of 2
- Jimmie did not catch the smallest fish

Who caught which fish

Jesse__22in_
Jacob_36in_
James__23in__
Jimmie__33in__
John_18in__

Catfish 23 in

Who wants Ice Cream?

Use the information provided below to determine fill in the missing data.

	Vanilla	Chocolate	Strawberry	Cookies & Crème
Sarah				X
Rachael			X	
Julia		X		
Deborah	X			

1. Rachel's favorite ice cream is either strawberry or chocolate
2. Sarah does not like vanilla ice cream
3. Deborah's favorite is either cookies and cream or vanilla
4. Julia's Favorite ice cream starts with the letter c

How Old am I?

Use the information provided below to determine fill in the missing data.

	30	31	32	33	34
Sarah		X			
Rachael					X
Julia			X		
Deborah			X		
Kia	X				

1. Sarah's age is a odd number
2. Rachel and Julia are one year apart
3. Rachel is the oldest
4. Kia is younger than Deborah

I love Jewels

Use the information provided below to determine fill in the missing data

	Gold	Silver	Diamond	Ruby	Pearl
Sarah		x			
Caitlin					x
Gina	x				
Tina			x		
Robin				x	

1. Sarah does not like gold or Pearls
2. Robin has jewelry that starts with the first letter of her name
3. Tina's great aunt gave her diamond earrings for Christmas last year
4. Gina likes silver or gold jewelry

What Day is it?

Use the calendar below to answer the following questions

Sunday	Monday	Tuesday	Wednesday	Thursday	Friday	Saturday
		1	2	3	4	5
6	7	8 X	9	10	11	12
13	14 X	15	16	17 X	18	19
20	21	22	23	24	25 X	26 X
27	28	29	30	31		

1. Work begins one week after the second Sunday. Mark that date with a blue marker 14th
2. The basketball game comes on the third Thursday. Place a x on that date. 17th
3. The doctors appointment is three weeks before the fifth Tuesday. Mark with date with a red marker 8th
4. What date is the 9 days after the third Wednesday? Mark that date with a green marker 25th
5. The picnic is the day after the 4th Friday. Mark that date with a black marker 26th

Patterns Everywhere!

Continue the pattern below

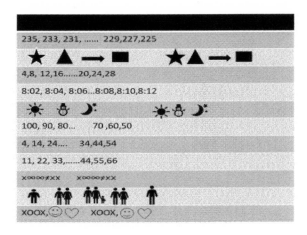

235, 233, 231, ... 229,227,225

★ ▲ → ■   ★ ▲ → ■

4,8, 12,16......20,24,28

8:02, 8:04, 8:06...8:08,8:10,8:12

☀ ☃ ☽   ☀ ☃ ☽

100, 90, 80...   70 ,60,50

4, 14, 24....   34,44,54

11, 22, 33,......44,55,66

x∞∞≠xx   x∞∞≠xx

👨👨👨👨👨   👨

xoox,☺♡   xoox,☺♡

Logic

Identify which item does not belong a each row

Logic
Identify which item does not belong n each row

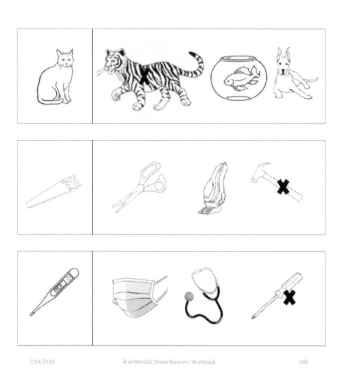

Logic
Identify which item does not belong n each row

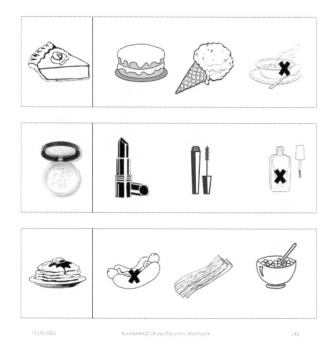

Logic
Identify which item does not belong n each row

Logic
Identify which item does not belong n each row

- Draw **a Red** ☐ around the animals
- Draw a **Blue X** on the things with wheels
- Draw a **Green** ◯ on the things you wear
- Draw and **Yellow** △ around things you eat

We Go together
Draw a line between the objects that go together

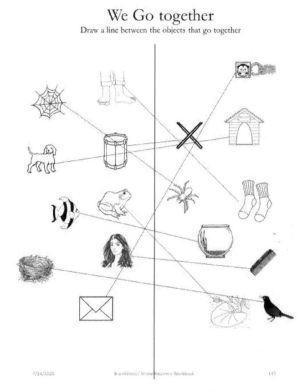

Made in the USA
Coppell, TX
05 November 2021